The Open University

Science: a level 3 course

Understanding the Continents

Block 5

Britain and global tectonics

Prepared for the Course Team by Steve Drury,
with contributions from Dave McGarvie, Ian Parkinson and Nigel Harris

Front Cover   Colour-coded image of topographic elevation for Scotland and Northern Ireland, incorporating simulated solar shading. Standing out clearly are several of the major boundaries between terranes that accreted to form the northern British Isles. They include the Great Glen, the Highland Boundary and Southern Uplands Faults. None show well on satellite images, largely because of the camouflaging effect of fields throughout much of the area. Data courtesy of the Landmap project, design by Steve Drury. Landmap is administered by MIMAS (http://landmap.ac.uk).

Rear Cover   James Hutton's famous unconformity at Siccar Point in Berwickshire, where horizontal terrestrial sandstones and conglomerates of Devonian age rest on vertical beds of Silurian turbidites, deformed during the last phase of the Caledonian orogeny.

The S339 Course team

Chair

Nigel Harris

Course Manager

Jessica Bartlett

Other members of the Course Team

Mandy Anton (Designer)

Tom Argles (Author)

Gerry Bearman (Editor)

Steve Blake (Block 3 Chair, Author)

Steve Drury (Block 5 Chair, Author)

Professor Wes Gibbons, University of Wales, Cardiff (Course Assessor)

Nigel Harris (Block 4 Chair, Author)

Lee Johnson (Graphic Artist)

Martin Kemp (BBC Producer)

Dave McGarvie (Author)

Jann Matela (Word Processing)

Ray Munns (Cartographer)

Pam Owen (Graphic Artist)

Ian Parkinson (Reader/Author)

Professor Julian Pearce, University of Wales, Cardiff (Course Assessor)

Nick Rogers (Block 2 Chair, Author)

Hazel Rymer (Block 1 Chair, Author)

Val Russell (original Course Manager)

Andy Sutton (Software Designer)

Peter Twomey (Editor)

John Whalley (Consultant Author, University of Portsmouth)

The Course Team gratefully acknowledges the contributions of those who produced the first editions of this Course, from which parts of this Block have been derived. In addition, we would like to thank the students, Associate Lecturers and assessors from other institutions who commented on drafts of this new edition. Other contributors to S339 are acknowledged in specific credits.

The Open University, Walton Hall, Milton Keynes MK7 6AA.

First published 2003.

Edited, designed and typeset by The Open University.

Printed in the United Kingdom by Bath Press, Blantyre Industrial Estate, Glasgow G72 0ND

ISBN 0 7492 5667 2

This block forms part of an Open University course, S339 Understanding the Continents. The complete list of texts which make up this course can be found at the back. Details of this and other Open University courses can be obtained from the Course Reservations and Sales Office, PO Box 724, The Open University, Milton Keynes MK7 6ZS, United Kingdom: tel. (00 44) 1908 653231. For availability of this or other course components, contact Open University Worldwide Ltd, Walton Hall, Milton Keynes MK7 6AA, United Kingdom: tel. (00 44) 1908 858585, fax (00 44) 1908 858787, e-mail ouwenq@open.ac.uk

Alternatively, much useful course information can be obtained from the Open University's website, http://www.open.ac.uk

3.1

Contents

1 Introduction

In earlier Blocks, you examined several key tectonic environments, in areas that we judge to illustrate many of the processes that operated in them. Each is an extensive, well-exposed region of active tectonics, where large-scale processes can be deduced with reasonable clarity. We have referred only occasionally to British geology, because the British Isles today lie within a tectonic plate, far from any active margin. Although the rocks here preserve evidence for rifting, mountain building, terrane accretion, volcanic arcs and even mantle plumes, the tectonic processes that gave rise to these features are no longer active. In this Block, you will use much of what you have learned from studying active examples to develop tectonic insights into ancient rocks that are closer to home. This will help you revise concepts from earlier in the Course. An abbreviated look at British geology is important, not only because it is here that you are most likely to observe geology in the field, but also because the British Isles were, in many ways, a cradle for the geological sciences — many of the concepts that underpin geological analysis stemmed from observations that were first made here.

Deciphering the history of our area's continental lithosphere is not just a matter of extracting information from rocks exposed at the surface. Many of the important lithologies outcrop only rarely, if at all, partly because of a vexing abundance of vegetation and veneers of glaciogenic debris, and partly because layers of structurally simple sedimentary rocks accumulated after major episodes of tectonic activity ceased. About a third of the crust underpinning Britain (very roughly to the south-east of a line between Berwick-upon-Tweed to Exeter) is hidden by this sedimentary cover, and so geophysical techniques provide a vital means to peer dimly through the surface layers to deeper levels. Section 2 (condensed from material produced by the late Geoff Brown for the predecessor version of this Course) introduces you to the use of geophysical data in assessing the broad structural make-up of the British lithosphere.

In the same way as the social and economic history of Britain only has true meaning in the light of unfolding world events, so a tectonic history of the British Isles without a context of the evolving Earth system as a whole is a dull catalogue of successive events that left their imprint here. Almost miraculously, our minuscule archipelago preserves one of the fullest records of global events anywhere. It does, however, omit sizeable chunks of the full story completely, from 4000–3000 Ma and 1750–1100 Ma. Moreover, it is inconceivable that everything that could and did happen to the lithospheric part of the Earth system left its mark in any one place. Section 3 serves to give you this broad overview of global tectonic evolution for the period after 900 Ma, that led to crust beneath the British Isles coming into being. Since we believe that you should be capable of grasping how Earth scientists arrived at this general context, the structure of Section 3 may appear a little odd at first sight. Parts of it proceed backwards in time, interspersed with sequences in 'fast-forward' mode. The thought experiment in Box 1.1 should help you grasp why such an approach is more realistic and useful than a simple story with a beginning, a middle and an end.

Box 1.1 The 'arrow of time' and building a geological history

Nearly everyone sees history as a sequence, beginning with the earliest, albeit sketchily known times, and unfolding towards progressively younger, better-known events. But that is what the historians *tell* us! Anyone who has studied how history is constructed will be well aware that the 'story' continually changes as more material comes to light, and as historians develop new analytical approaches to those data. We, the readers, see only the syntheses that individual historians write! Historians (and Earth scientists) have as much trouble with recent events as they do with those in the distant past. Neither has the luxury of any certainties.

Archaeology is especially instructive, because it is literally 'delving into the past'. A 'dig' always goes backwards in time, from one level to a deeper level.

● How would you proceed to work out a sequence of events when presented with a geological map that lacked a detailed legend — a 'problem' map?

● You would start with the latest and simplest events, generally a veneer of structurally simple sedimentary rocks — a young cover. Beneath that you might find an unconformity above structurally more complicated, older sedimentary rocks — an older cover. Given sufficient topographic relief, there would probably be a folded unconformity beneath that, on top of what early geologists once called 'The Fundamental Complex', the crystalline stuff of the continental crust proper; literally the bottom! Even in an area subjected to repeated deformation and metamorphism, you might derive data that separate its history into distinct events — generally going backwards to the ever more obscure. In any one area, there is a limit to how far back the rocks can take you; there is a 'beginning', before which any materials of the lithosphere were unable to resist oblivion through subduction.

Geologists have always 'mined' time, rather than floating upwards through it — downwards and backwards to increasing complexity and increasing uncertainty. The stories that they tell are not 'correct', but change as the 'mining' progresses, often dramatically so. The material available for synthesis into a sense of geological history increases as new techniques and new concepts emerge. The development in the 1960s and 1970s of plate-tectonic ideas, and the techniques that made them possible, transformed previous notions of geological evolution out of all recognition.

Another aspect of geological research is the geographically sideways expansion of knowledge, and the ideas that it supports. Some areas have more intricate, better preserved and longer sequences of past events than those, such as the British Isles, where the first work went on. They only come to light through exploration. Knowledge and ideas from 'time mining' in previously uncharted areas, invariably feed back to the older sources of data. And, equally inevitably, the 'story' or synthesis of discoveries becomes ever more detailed. Hopefully, it converges on what really happened, but the plate-tectonic revolution is an object lesson in never grimly hanging on to the 'old story'!

The history of any segment of the continental lithosphere is not divorced from those of all the rest — this is the single most important lesson learned from the discovery of plate tectonics. Earth scientists have used various techniques to chart tectonics from the well-known modern framework to those of less-certain, earlier times. Section 3 outlines this to prepare you for an up-to-date synthesis of the story of the British lithosphere in later Sections. An important theme in Section 3 concerns how it has become increasingly certain that much of Earth history, most clearly from the end of the Mesoproterozoic (about 1100 Ma ago) until now, involved a series of amalgamations of almost all continental lithosphere and the eventual break-up of these supercontinents. Much of British tectonic evolution stems from that period, and Section 3 provides a global context for your study of Sections 5 and 6.

There are examples of even earlier rocks in the British Isles, but interpreting tectonics during the Archean* (before 2500 Ma ago) needs a cautious approach. In the case of the Lewisian Complex (Section 4), and similar high-grade metamorphic rocks of any age, there is a limit to deducing the tectonic environments in which they formed from the geological features that they display. That is largely because they contain few, if any, rocks that preserve unambiguous signs of their origins. Understanding them relies on their structures and their geochemistry. Caution is also wise when looking at barely deformed or metamorphosed Archean rocks from other cratons, because magmatic processes and the manner in which the lithosphere deformed and re-entered the mantle during the Earth's early history may have been different from those in later times. The reason for this is the Earth's greater production of heat from radioactive decay earlier in its history, and the possible effects of that on magmatism, the lithosphere's strength and the way subduction affected it. These are the driving forces for tectonics, and theory suggests that major processes may have been different under changed thermal conditions. Section 4 looks at the distinct possibility that the Earth did not always behave according to James Hutton's Principle of Uniformitarianism.

The last two Sections move forward through the evolution of the British Isles during the Neoproterozoic and Phanerozoic. That evolution is almost certainly a direct result of tectonic processes with which you should now be familiar. Section 5 shows how orogenic events driven by the global motions outlined in Section 3 assembled the British Isles from several separate lithospheric blocks, both large and small, culminating at the end of the Paleozoic Era. This relates to what you studied in Blocks 3 and 4. A great deal of variation in the sedimentary history of the British Isles went on during the Upper Paleozoic, Mesozoic and Cenozoic Eras. However, this was due to episodes of broad lithospheric extension, ups and downs of global sea-level and only small-scale lithospheric shortening events. Such essentially surface processes are outside the scope of this Course. However, twice in this tectonically quiet stage, mantle melting dominated the scene, first as a result of Carboniferous rifting in the Midland Valley, and finally during the Tertiary, when the British lithosphere almost became the site of the North Atlantic constructive margin, as Pangaea broke apart. Section 6 uses these British examples to help you revise Block 2.

* Terms such as 'Archean', 'Paleozoic', etc. may also be spelled 'Archaean', 'Palaeozoic', etc. In most other OU Earth Science Courses, we use 'ae' rather than the 'e' adopted in S339 and continued in this Block for consistency. It is acceptable for you to use whichever spelling you prefer.

2 Geological 'anatomy' of the British Isles

This Section is condensed from Lithosphere Geophysics in Britain, *Block 1B of the original S339, written by the late Geoff Brown.*

A tour of the British Isles reveals a couple of obvious features that relate to their underlying geology. The first is that seeing rocks is a very occasional experience, except along some parts of the coast, in stream beds, and on a few rugged hills. Being moist, the British Isles are cloaked in vegetation. Having been glaciated repeatedly over the last 2.5 Ma, a blanket of ice-transported debris drapes over most of the terrain north of Watford, even on many hills. Land to the south of the Pleistocene ice front is mantled by all manner of river-deposited sediments and debris formed over ground that underwent repeated freezing and thawing. Compared with arid to semi-arid areas and truly mountainous regions, the British Isles is not an ideal place to deduce Earth history. However, until the end of the 19th century it was here that much geological theory developed. The reason for that is economic, for many resources on which the Industrial Revolution depended were those won from rocks — coal, ironstones, building materials, groundwater and so forth. The communications which industrial expansion demanded — canals and railways — cut deeply through its superficial mask to expose rocks to early geologists. Necessity more or less invented geology in Britain, and geologists have rummaged through that early legacy ever since.

The first geological maps, beginning with that of England and Wales made in 1801 by William Smith, roughly charted areas where industry and population grew most quickly (east of a line from Berwick to Exeter); the sedimentary strata of Upper Paleozoic (Devonian, Carboniferous and Permian), Mesozoic (Triassic, Jurassic and Cretaceous) and Cenozoic age. For the most part, these important repositories of physical resources are structurally simple. By defining broad folds and the effects of simple faults, this simplicity enabled early geologists to predict locations where known resources might be found.

West of the notional line, geologists at first found themselves nonplussed by the rocks there. Altogether more complex in structure, they comprised a mixed bag: sediments with very different and more primitive fossils (those of Cambrian, Ordovician and Silurian age), igneous rocks and large tracts where original sedimentary and igneous features had been obliterated by deformation and metamorphism, particularly in northern Scotland and NW Ireland. This 'Fundamental Complex', turned out literally to be at the 'bottom of things'. The first step in recognizing what it represented was James Hutton's discovery of at first perplexing boundaries, where structurally simple sediments are found above the underlying 'Fundamental Complex'. Eventually, Hutton grasped that these unconformities signify gaps in time, between whatever had contributed to the complexity beneath and the processes of deposition that had laid down the upper, sedimentary strata. He and succeeding geologists of the 19th century proposed that unconformities reflected long periods of erosion following transformation and upheaval of the lower, older rocks by orogenesis (literally the 'becoming of mountains' from the Greek *oros* for 'mountain' and *gignomai* for 'become'). The worn-down, almost planar landscape of eroded mountains became the base for the eventual deposition of much younger sediments.

This meaning of unconformities remains the single most important key to charting the evolution of the continents. Each graphically represents real events that segment rock associations and their formative processes in terms of relative time. Careful mapping of geological boundaries on all continents revealed dozens of unconformities with varying degrees of significance.

Apportioning Phanerozoic time, since 544 Ma ago, into globally recognized Periods depended on finding fossils at a similar stage of evolution in far-separated sedimentary rocks. The stratigraphic levels where fossils record sudden changes (now known to be products of mass-extinction events) were used as boundaries between the different Eras, Periods and lesser divisions of relative time. In some cases, these paleontological boundaries coincided with unconformities. Stratigraphic nomenclature is a shorthand for both organic and inorganic evolution, rather than arbitrary 'pigeonholing'. For those rocks formed before the emergence of organisms with hard parts — during the Precambrian — unconformities were the sole means of time division, until the development of accurate means of radiometric dating (effectively only since the late 1950s). Absolute dates permit Earth scientists to chart events in numerical terms and to establish the rates of processes. However, billions and even millions of years are simply unimaginable, and geologists can grasp events only in relation to one another.

Britain is blessed with just three unconformities of any consequence (Figure 2.1), which bear witness to three orogenies:

1   That preceding the deposition of Neoproterozoic continental sandstones of the Torridonian. This produced the Lewisian Complex, the focus of Section 4, where you will discover that it represents a multiplicity of crust-forming and crust-modifying events spanning more than a billion years.

(a)

(b)

(c)

Figure 2.1   Photographs of unconformities. (a) Torridonian. From left to right, the hills Suilven, Canisp and Cuil More in the Assynt district of Sutherland, Scotland. Each is an isolated pile of horizontal Torridonian sandstones that rest on an irregular unconformity. The low ground exposes Lewisian gneisses, and the 'knobbly' present surface is in fact an exhumed, one billion-year-old landscape. (b) Horizontal Devonian red sandstones above vertical Silurian turbidites at James Hutton's famous locality at Siccar Point, near St Abbs, Berwickshire. (c) Permian red conglomerates above steeply dipping, reddened Devonian turbidites with quartz veins at Salton Cove, near Paignton, Devon.

2 Events that deformed and metamorphosed sediments laid down at roughly the same time as the Torridonian sandstones and until Late Silurian times. In reality, these rocks of the Scottish Highlands and the west of the British Isles preserve evidence for several orogenic events; but in Section 5 we shall concentrate mainly on the latest of these events, for the rocks reveal evidence for the evolutionary history of a major ocean and rocks on both its flanks. This is the Caledonian orogeny, marked by the unconformity beneath (and in some places within) Devonian sediments, except in SW England.

3 The unconformity at the base of the Permian, becoming more profound in SW England, marks the eroded structures of an orogeny that dominates much of Europe south of Britain — the Variscan. This latest major unconformity is essentially the base on which Britain's Mesozoic and Cenozoic sedimentary cover built up without significant interruption by later tectonic events.

A quick glance at the *Tectonic Map of Britain, Ireland and Adjacent Areas* (called 'Tectonic Map' from now on) shows how irritating unconformities are for those concerned with visualizing the make-up of continental crust. The sedimentary cover above the last two unconformities more or less completely obscures deeper crustal levels, and isolates those of its occurrences from which this veneer has vanished. The next Section explores ways in which geophysical information reflects features of the buried deeper crust.

2.1   Geophysical pictures of the British Isles

The two most easily measured potential fields that are detectable everywhere at the Earth's surface are gravitational and magnetic. Both vary because of changes in physical properties of rocks beneath the surface. Surveys of these fields are keys to understanding large structures beneath the continents that juxtapose rocks with contrasted properties. Interpreting results from potential-field surveys can be of two kinds:

1 Modelling involves matching the forms taken by natural variations with those that can be predicted mathematically from bodies of rocks with different properties, which are inferred to occur at depth. This requires considerable computing power, sophisticated software and specialized skills. To have any meaning, models of this kind must match surface geology, and they must obey basic geological 'rules'. Modelling works only over small areas with a few distinct features in potential-field data.

2 The other approach is to interpret potential-field variations in a qualitative way over large areas. Again that depends on geological 'common sense', together with a broad understanding of how changing physical properties in the subsurface manifest themselves in the force fields measured at the surface.

You will engage in some 'broad-brush' interpretations of potential-field data for Britain later, using the *Gravity* and *Magnetic Anomaly Maps of Britain, Ireland and Adjacent Areas* (GRAV and MAG from now on) in relation to the Tectonic Map. First, you need some basic information about how geophysicists produced GRAV and MAG (Box 2.1).

Box 2.1 Image-maps of potential-field data

Potential-field values at survey points, in the case of gravity, and along lines surveyed from aircraft, as in magnetic surveys, are samples of continuous variations in the field over the surface. Mathematically fitting a three-dimensional surface (two geographic dimensions plus the variable itself) to these known changes in a potential field approximates the real variation. In effect, such surfaces are 'images' of the potential field, in the same sense as a camera captures the variation in light reflected by a surface. Until the widespread availability of powerful graphics software, such interpolations formed the basis for drawing contour maps. However, to our eyes such maps appear as variations in the spacing of the contours, which gives varying brightness that signifies changes in the *gradient* of the field — that is why contoured topographic maps are difficult to interpret. Displaying the same data on computer monitors, as if they are really images, matches them to our vision.

On such image-maps, high values of a potential field produce bright signatures and low ones are dark. The human eye is not particularly good at visualizing different grey tones, but is extremely efficient at distinguishing colours. So, GRAV and MAG show varying field intensities as a variant of the familiar rainbow spectrum. The 'cool' colours, blue to green, represent low values and 'warm' yellow to red correspond to increasingly high values. Another means of bringing out the information content is to simulate the effects of shadowing, as if the modelled surface was in fact topography illuminated from a particular direction at a specific angle. That imparts visual clues to the shape of the surface, converting a visually bland variation into one to which evolution has tuned the human visual system. Many subtle features snap into sharp relief when we look at such 'shaded-relief' images. The GRAV and MAG maps combine such illumination from the north with colour coding of the actual values (see the Key). They also show contours, the important ones being emboldened.

Gravity varies according to differences in density. Magnetic-field variations chart differences in magnetic susceptibility. In the case of some parts of the crust, varying polarity in the intensity of remanent magnetization from the distant past also affects the magnetic field.

2.1.1 Gravity data

Box 2.2 summarizes how anomalies in the gravitational field relate to variations in density beneath the Earth's surface.

Box 2.2 Gravity anomalies

The acceleration due to gravity (g) at any point on the Earth's surface depends on the proportion of the Earth's mass that lies along a line passing downwards to the centre of the Earth. If the Earth was both a uniform sphere and contained exactly the same rocks in shells concentric around its centre, then its gravitational field would be the same everywhere. If there is a lower proportion of mass below a point at the surface than expected from this simple model, due to rocks that are less dense than surrounding ones, that reduces g at the point relative to the model's prediction. In other words, there would be a *negative anomaly*. Conversely, denser rocks beneath the point would produce a *positive anomaly*. Things are somewhat more complicated than that, however!

The Earth is not a uniform sphere, its radius at the equator being larger than at the poles. So g increases by about 0.5% from equator to the poles, and gravity surveys require a standard correction for latitude. The Earth's surface is not smooth, of course. Because gravitational force varies inversely with the square of distance, the higher the elevation of a survey point the lower g would be for a uniform sphere, and that means another correction, which standardizes gravity to the accepted mean sea-level. Deviations from the average density of upper continental crust ($2700\,kg\,m^{-3}$) then show as anomalies. The result from these and other corrections is known as the Bouguer gravity value, or **Bouguer anomaly**, which is zero where g is exactly as predicted by the modelling involved. Negative values indicate an underlying mass deficiency, due to lower overall density, whereas a positive Bouguer anomaly indicates excess mass and high density.

The influence of a contrast in density expands and lessens with distance from it. A small, extremely dense sphere — such as a buried iron meteorite — at a shallow depth will produce a locally sharp, positive anomaly. With increasing burial, the anomaly's peak value decreases and the anomalous feature becomes broader. There is a rule of thumb that the width of a gravity anomaly at half its amplitude ('height') is about twice the depth to its source, if it is due to a small, anomalously dense body, and less if the body is extensive. Few features of the continental lithosphere that show clearly on Bouguer anomaly images are broader than 100 km across, and so they represent density variations in the top 50 km of the lithosphere. The majority of anomaly patterns are smaller than this and have sources in the upper 20 km of the crust. Your first examination of GRAV will reveal this general limitation to the upper crust.

The best way of introducing you to the way in which major crustal features of Britain affect gravity data is to focus on an area whose geology you may know from attending residential schools based in Durham (Figure 2.2). The area is bounded by longitudes 1° and 5° W and latitudes 53.4° and 55.6° N, so you can easily find it on GRAV. Simulated illumination from the north gives the illusion of highlighted northwards slopes and shadowed slopes that face southwards, that together with the colour coding picks out local highs and lows in the anomaly pattern. Positive anomalies show as green through yellow to red and negative ones as green to dark blue. The zero anomaly is in the greens (see the Key), and is also shown as a bold contour.

> **Question 2.1** Locate the Permo-Triassic basin of the Vale of Eden, and the Pennine Fault on GRAV. What is the gravity 'signature' of this structure, and what might cause it?

⬤ Are there any similar features on GRAV that might also relate to other Permo-Triassic basins on Figure 2.2?

◔ Yes, there are two such basins near Dumfries, with similar anomaly signatures to that associated with the Vale of Eden.

Notice that the Permo-Triassic strata that outcrop east and south-east of Durham do not show anomalies, but are part of a regional gravity low that extends N–S down the east side of the Pennine Hills. This is the western flank of the North Sea sedimentary basin that is filled with Carboniferous and younger sediments, which become thicker eastwards. Considerable thicknesses of Carboniferous rocks underlie the Permo-Triassic of the eastern part of northern England. The Vale of Eden and Dumfries basins show up strongly because they are fault-bounded outliers on thin (Vale of Eden) or absent (Dumfries) Carboniferous

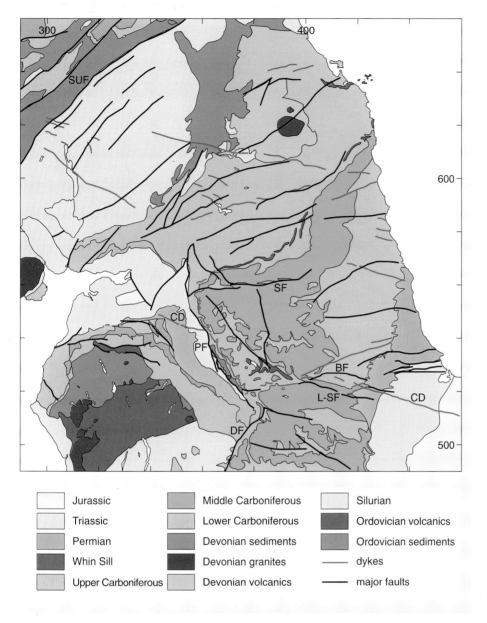

Figure 2.2 Outline geology of Northern England and the Southern Uplands of Scotland. Faults: SUF Southern Uplands Fault; PF Pennine Fault; SF Stublick Fault; BF Butterknowle Fault; L–SF Lunedale–Staindrop Fault; DF Dent Fault. Dyke: CD Cleveland Dyke.

Legend:
- Jurassic
- Triassic
- Permian
- Whin Sill
- Upper Carboniferous
- Middle Carboniferous
- Lower Carboniferous
- Devonian sediments
- Devonian granites
- Devonian volcanics
- Silurian
- Ordovician volcanics
- Ordovician sediments
- dykes
- major faults

strata above the lightly metamorphosed and denser sedimentary and volcanic rocks of the Lower Paleozoic in the Lake District and Southern Uplands. These older rocks that outcrop in the west sometimes show positive anomalies, but not always.

Question 2.2 One of the central issues at the Level 2 Geology summer school was seeking explanations for variations in the thickness and facies of the Lower Carboniferous beneath the Pennines. The Alston and Askrigg Blocks are overlain by thin, cyclical build-ups deposited in shallow water, and are separated by basins with thicker, deeper-water sediments of the same age. What is thought to underlie the two blocks, and do they have a signature on GRAV? Are there other gravitational features that might have a similar interpretation?

● To which geological feature on the Tectonic Map does the linear set of gravity anomalies at the NW of the limits to Figure 2.2 correspond?

● This relates to the Southern Uplands Fault, separating the mainly Upper Paleozoic strata of the Midland Valley of Scotland from the Lower Paleozoic rocks of the Southern Uplands.

● Can you explain the trend from negative regional Bouguer anomaly in the east to positive anomaly in the west of Figure 2.2?

● The eastern half is dominated by increasing thickness of Upper Paleozoic to Cenozoic sedimentary rocks towards the North Sea basin. The west is dominated by either thin cover or exposed Lower Paleozoic rocks.

The foregoing should have given you an impression of the gravitational 'signatures' of four fundamental aspects of crustal structure: sedimentary basins; varying thickness of low density cover over denser basement; major faults; and large granitic intrusions. Before going on to build on them in revealing tectonic features of the whole of Britain and adjacent areas in Activity 2.1, you will repeat the exercise in the next Section, for magnetic data.

2.1.2 Magnetic data

Box 2.3 summarizes how anomalies in the magnetic field relate to different magnetic properties of rocks in the crust.

Box 2.3 Magnetic anomalies

The Earth's magnetic field is similar to that produced by a bar magnet (Figure 2.3). It originates in the core, more than 2900 km down, and is very roughly aligned with the axis of rotation. At high latitudes, lines of magnetic force plunge steeply into the Earth, and this magnetic inclination decreases towards the equator where it is horizontal. As with gravitational acceleration, the overall picture is not uniform, because the Earth is not a perfect dipole magnet. Corrections to magnetic field data use a mathematical model expressing gross (and changing) features of the geomagnetic field. It is this correction that reveals departures from the expected values. Magnetic anomalies are due to buried bodies of magnetized rock that locally distort the Earth's overall field. It is principally randomly distributed iron oxide and sulphide minerals that become magnetized in rocks, and their proportions vary according to the rocks' composition.

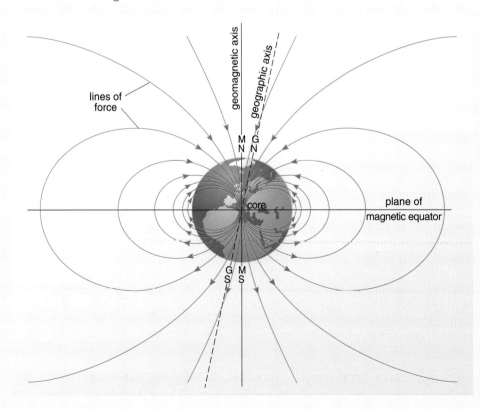

Figure 2.3 Section through the axis of the Earth's dipolar magnetic field showing notional lines of force. The arrows close to the Earth's surface show how the inclination of the field varies with latitude. Note the difference between the axis of rotation joining the geographic poles (GN and GS), and the magnetic axis joining the shifting magnetic poles (MN and MS).

Magnetic minerals can become magnetized in two ways. The present-day geomagnetic field induces magnetization, to produce an **induced magnetic field** that has the opposite polarity to that of the Earth. The induced poles become north- and south-seeking (the Earth's north pole is a south-seeking pole). The significance of this will become clear shortly. Induced polarity can change with the Earth's field, in direction (because the magnetic poles move) and in polarity during magnetic reversal events. However, part of this induced field becomes permanently imprinted in the minerals involved at the moment that they form, either by crystallizing in an igneous or metamorphic rock, or when they settle as grains within a sediment. That lingering field is **remanent magnetization**, and reflects the direction and inclination of the Earth's field at the time of a rock's formation. Remanent magnetization is the key to charting past continental positions in relation to latitude (Block 1, and Section 3 of this Block). It also reflects the Earth's polarity at the time of permanent magnetization, which has a roughly 50 : 50 chance of having been reversed or normal in the past.

An important issue with respect to both remanent and induced magnetization in crystalline rocks is that neither can occur if the temperature is too high, for molecular vibration reduces the susceptibility of minerals to becoming magnetic. The upper limit is between 400 and 600 °C (the Curie point), depending on the mineral.

- How much of the continental lithosphere is able to influence magnetic-field anomalies if the geothermal gradient is 20 °C km^{-1}?

- Temperature will reach the Curie point between 20 and 30 km beneath the Earth's surface, so only variations in the magnetic susceptibility of rocks in the crust have any effect.

The amplitude and breadth of magnetic anomalies decrease and broaden with increasing distance to their source, in a similar manner to those in the gravitational field. Like gravity anomalies, most magnetic anomalies reflect features in the upper crust. However, their shapes are quite different. This is because the induced and geomagnetic fields interfere. They do this because dipolar magnetism has a different kind of directionality from that of gravity. Gravitational force is always radially towards the centre of a massive body. A dipolar magnetic field follows notional lines joining the poles (Figure 2.3), and its direction depends on position relative to both poles and the form taken by these notional lines of magnetic force. Figure 2.4 shows how local and regional magnetic fields interfere to produce magnetic anomalies.

The geomagnetic field is simple at a local to regional scale, provided there are no variations in the magnetic properties of the crust beneath. Lines of force represent it as a uniformly dipping field with a direction. By convention this is taken as downwards

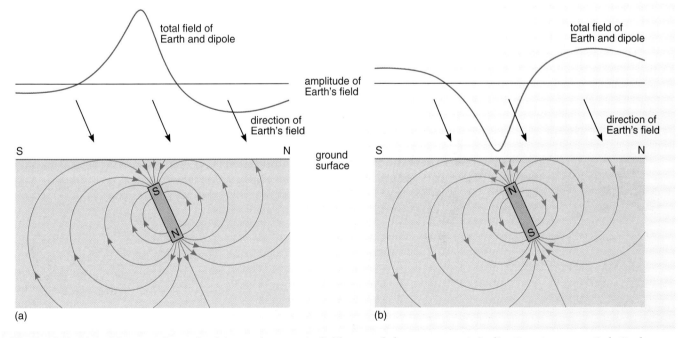

Figure 2.4 (a) South to north graph of the total magnetic-field strength for geomagnetic inclination at a magnetic latitude of 68° N, above (a) a magnetic body with an induced dipole; (b) a body with a dipolar remanent field produced during a period of reversed geomagnetic field.

in the Northern Hemisphere (the Earth's north magnetic pole is a south-seeking pole) and upwards in the Southern Hemisphere. At the magnetic equator, lines of magnetic force are horizontal and northwards (Figure 2.3). Magnetization induced in unusually magnetic bodies has its polarity imposed by the local geomagnetic field and is parallel to it. That is, it has the same sense of polarity with a south-seeking pole at its northern pole and *vice versa*. The combined effect of the geomagnetic and induced fields is therefore somewhat complicated, because the induced field takes on a similar form to that of a small bar magnet while the geomagnetic field is locally simple. Where regional and anomalous magnetic fields have the same direction, they reinforce one another and produce a stronger field. Where opposed, the induced field reduces the overall field. Only where the direction of the induced field is at right angles to the geomagnetic field is there no anomaly. Figure 2.4a shows the effect for a short dipole where the geomagnetic field is steeply dipping downwards at high northern latitudes. Figure 2.4b shows the opposite result for a remanent dipole formed during a period of reversed geomagnetic polarity.

● Apart from the different shapes of the two graphs in Figure 2.4, what two features are common to both?

● The graphs show paired positive and negative anomalies. Neither of the anomalies lies directly over the source.

The first feature makes images of magnetic anomalies more complicated than those for gravity anomaly. The second hinders relating an anomaly to its source, unlike gravity anomalies, which lie over their sources. A third difficulty is that anomalies formed by bodies with induced or remanent magnetization appear superficially similar. Worse still, Figure 2.4 is for the simplest geological case — a short dipolar magnet, which is the form likely for a small magnetic sphere. Bodies of magnetic rock can take on many shapes — irregular igneous intrusions, vertical or horizontal sheets of igneous rocks or magnetically susceptible sediments with different orientations relative to the geomagnetic field, and many more. Shape variation will affect the positions and separations of the induced poles in such bodies, and so the shape of the induced magnetic field.

With these caveats about an admittedly very complex topic, you can familiarize yourself with basic interpretation of magnetic data by looking again at the regional geology of Northern England (Figure 2.2) in relation to the corresponding area on MAG.

You will notice that MAG for this area looks very different from GRAV. In particular, there is a much smaller proportion of magnetically positive areas. This is because a great deal of the area is underlain to depths of several kilometres by sedimentary cover. Magnetic minerals (iron-rich oxides and sulphides) form in igneous rocks, and sometimes as a result of metamorphism, but only rarely as a product of diagenesis of sediments. They break down to non-magnetic minerals under the oxidizing conditions of subaerial erosion and transportation. When crystalline rocks are weathered and eroded, dense mineral grains (all magnetic minerals have high density) remain close to their source, so that sediments deposited far from their source have much lower contents of magnetic grains than do crystalline rocks. Whatever their source, sediments have weak magnetic properties — enough so that their weak remanent magnetization can be measured in hand specimens, but insufficient for them to bear much induced magnetization.

The other contrast with gravity data is that MAG shows different anomaly patterns. The most striking are narrow, long and very nearly straight.

● In the northern half of the area covered by Figure 2.2, there are several sharp linear features that run WNW–ESE, roughly parallel to one another. Can you suggest what they might be?

● These are part of a Tertiary swarm of thick basaltic dykes that emanate from the islands of Mull and Skye off NW Scotland (Section 6.2). The most south-westerly of these, and the most prominent, is the Cleveland dyke that you may have examined at Level 2 Geology Residential School.

For most of its length, the Cleveland dyke does not outcrop, being buried beneath soil and glacial drift, but it lies only a few metres below the surface. That is why it and other swarm members show such strong anomalies — linear, north-seeking poles of strongly magnetic bodies lie just beneath the surface (their south-seeking poles are at the bottom of the vertical sheets, perhaps as much as 20 km down, and so their magnetic effect is minimal).

Another very prominent linear feature on MAG runs ENE–WSW in the NW part of the area of Figure 2.2. This is the magnetic trace of the Southern Uplands Fault, and is so prominent because outcrops of highly magnetic, Upper Paleozoic lavas occur on its downthrow side, to the NNW. Faults express themselves by magnetic anomalies if they displace sheets of strongly magnetic rock that dip at shallow angles. In the case of a dip-slip fault, either erosion has stripped the layer from the upthrow side so that it produces a strong anomaly on the downthrow side (Southern Uplands Fault), or the layer occurs higher in the crust on the upthrow side, so expressing itself more sharply than on the more deeply buried downthrow side. Strike–slip faults shift bodies with all kinds of magnetic properties laterally, and this produces a linear break in the magnetic 'grain' that would otherwise be continuous.

- One of the major faults that influenced the sedimentary evolution of the Carboniferous strata west of Durham is the Butterknowle Fault (Figure 2.2). Does it show up?

- There is a definite WSW–ENE feature trending from Teesside to the south of the Vale of Eden. This coincides with the Butterknowle Fault, and the splayed faults that connect it with the Pennine Fault in the Brough area show as a disjointed series of short WNW–ESE linear features at its western end.

There are several other linear features that do not run parallel to the trend of the Tertiary dykes. One extends to the ENE from the northern side of the Solway Firth towards Berwick-upon-Tweed. This is a major fault on the north flank of the Northumberland–Solway Basin that began to fill in the Carboniferous. When you examine the regional variations in magnetic anomaly on MAG, you will see the linear anomalies related to Tertiary dyke swarms very clearly, in this area extending SE into the southern North Sea, a set trending E–W in the North Sea off the east coast of Southern Scotland, and running NW–SE across Northern Ireland and the Irish Sea.

Question 2.3 Figure 2.2 shows the various granitic masses in this part of Britain. You saw in Question 2.2 how deeply buried granitic masses express themselves on the gravity image. How do the exposed and buried granites appear in that part of MAG which covers Figure 2.2? Try to come up with explanations for granite-related features.

Magnetic data present some conundrums, such as the magnetic ridge extending WNW through the Yorkshire Dales to the Lake District — is it granite or is it some other kind of crystalline basement at shallow levels? It is not possible to say with certainty, except that the gravity low that forms the evidence for a granite beneath the Askrigg Block (Question 2.2) coincides with the highest magnetic anomaly in the area, and the trend does lead to areas of the Lake District where granites outcrop. Similar magnetic highs are present beneath the central Irish Sea and running parallel to regional strike in the western part of the Southern Uplands.

- Look at the area on GRAV and MAG south of the Ribble estuary and in the Cheshire Plain. Can you explain the anomalies there?

● A circular, positive magnetic anomaly coincides with a positive gravity anomaly. Both anomalies have the same source, which must be magnetic and dense. This cannot be a granite beneath the Permo-Triassic rocks of Lancashire. The source may be a mafic intrusion in the basement.

The last prominent magnetic feature in the area of Figure 2.2 is a strong, arcuate anomaly with positive values in the northern Lake District. This is easily explained by surface geology, as it coincides with outcrops of the Lower Ordovician Eycott lavas of basaltic and basaltic andesite composition — generally rich in magnetic minerals. These are pillow lavas that erupted on the sea floor. The magnetic anomaly continues beyond the outcropping Eycott lavas, which are overstepped by Carboniferous strata, to the Solway coast. Note that the main Ordovician lavas, the felsic Borrowdale Volcanic Group of the central Lake District, are not magnetic, and have an associated negative magnetic anomaly.

Activity 2.1

This Activity builds on what you have learned from considering gravity and magnetic data in relation to a geological map. You will be comparing features on GRAV and MAG with the Tectonic Map that summarizes the geology of the British Isles. You should allow about two hours for this Activity.

Figure 2.5 summarizes the most important elements of surface geology and structure in the British Isles, which the Tectonic Map shows in much more detail, with additional information. You will find it a useful reference throughout the rest of Section 2.

Gravity and magnetic data help divide the British Isles into a number of distinct crustal provinces that broadly relate to fundamental aspects of surface geology. From Section 4 onwards you will be looking specifically at the tectonic processes that formed these provinces, using direct geological evidence. Potential-field data give an inkling of deep crustal structure, but one that can only be modelled imprecisely and ambiguously. They give blurred clues to variations with depth in the crust that are sufficiently intriguing to seek detail in the vertical dimension. That is possible using seismic experiments.

2.1.3 Summary of Section 2.1

* Maps or images of gravitational and magnetic potential field, when processed to allow for broad variations that are unconnected with the geology of the crust, reveal variations in the density and magnetic properties of buried rocks as anomalies.

* On both gravity and magnetic images, the more deeply buried the source of an anomaly is, the broader and lower in amplitude is the anomaly at the surface. In a general way, the width of an anomaly above a small source (e.g. a small intrusion) is equivalent to twice the depth to its source. This is due to an inverse-square relationship between field strength and source depth.

* The Bouguer gravity anomaly map of the British Isles (GRAV) reveals depositional basins of the Younger Cover, and low density bodies (probably granitic intrusions) in the basement beneath it as negative anomalies. Large faults show as linear features separating different anomaly patterns.

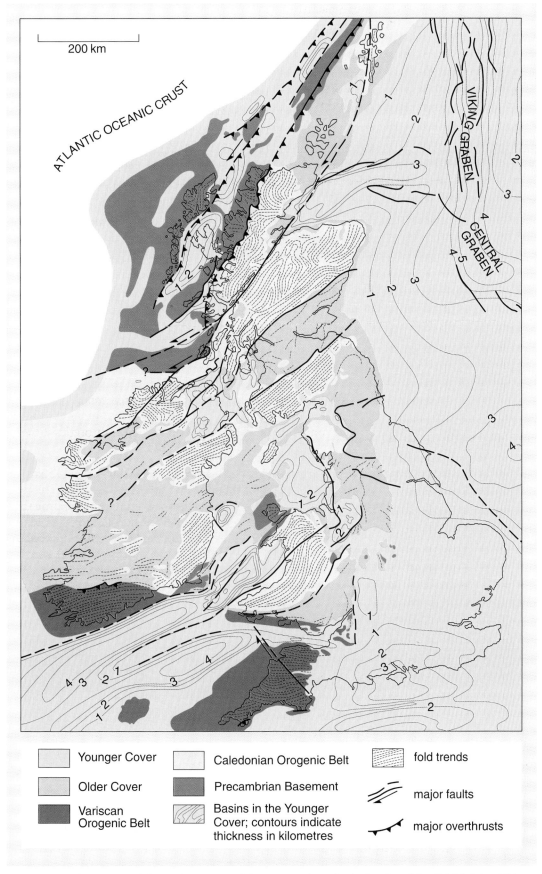

Figure 2.5   Summary of the main structural features and geological units of the British Isles. This may prove useful as a 'thumbnail' of the Tectonic Map.

- The magnetic anomaly map of the British Isles (MAG) shows deep sedimentary basins of the Younger and Older Cover as broad, smooth areas of negative anomaly, due to the low abundance of magnetic minerals in sedimentary rocks. Areas where the basement or igneous rocks outcrop or are close to the surface are magnetically 'rough' because the Earth's magnetic field induces dipoles in their higher content of magnetic minerals. This process highlights shallow igneous intrusions, even quite small ones. By displacing magnetic rocks, faults produce linear breaks in the regional magnetic 'grain', as well as separating areas with different magnetic roughness.

- Features on GRAV and MAG formed the basis for much of the analysis of deep crustal structure that appears on the Tectonic Map, particularly in areas of Younger and Older Cover.

2.2 Seismic evidence for the British Isles' deep-crustal structure

The deep structure of the Earth as a whole emerged from studies of arrival times at a world-wide network of seismographs that record body waves from natural earthquakes. Seismic experiments to detect and map small-scale features of the crust depend on similar principles, with two important differences. They use energy produced by a variety of artificial means that generate much weaker body waves than those involved in earthquakes, and they detect wave arrivals with linear arrays of many sensitive detectors, or geophones.

Figure 2.6 shows how seismic waves travel through layered rocks, in terms of the speed at which they propagate seismic energy. Boundaries between rocks with different wave speeds reflect some of the energy back to the surface. How much is reflected depends on the angle of incidence and on the sharpness and nature of the boundary. A proportion of the seismic energy penetrates such boundaries to travel in rock with a different speed of wave propagation. The direction in which waves travel once they have passed through a speed boundary depends on two things: the angle of incidence, and the difference in speed between the adjoining layers. The second is vital, because it changes the direction of propagation by a process of refraction. A useful rule of thumb is that *refraction shifts the travel path of a seismic wave towards the layer with the lower speed of propagation.* You can see this in Figure 2.6a; waves travel through the lower layer at higher speed, so refraction is upwards. In this case, the wave travels progressively deeper in the lower layer, because it was originally travelling steeply downwards in the upper layer, but the angle relative to the surface is smaller. The implication of refraction of this kind is that as the angle of incidence at the boundary becomes larger, so the refracted wave travels at a decreased angle to the boundary. Eventually, at a critical angle of incidence the refracted wave travels parallel to the boundary (Figure 2.6b). At higher incidence angles, little energy penetrates the boundary, and most is reflected towards the surface (Figure 2.6c).

Using seismic energy to probe the deep structure of the crust takes two forms: seismic refraction methods, which detect energy refracted by layers with different wave-propagation speeds, and seismic reflection methods that detect the energy reflected by crustal layers. Reflection merely requires a boundary between rocks with different properties, so profiles based on reflection record many waves returning from sharp boundaries between layers. Refraction surveys depend on detecting the first arrival of energy at a detector.

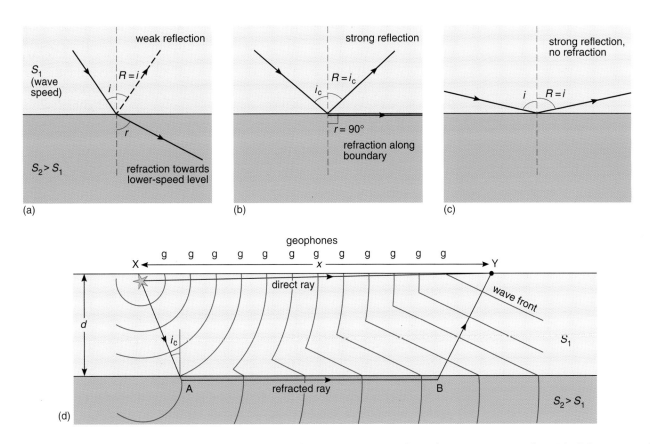

Figure 2.6   Diagrams showing reflection and refraction of seismic energy at a boundary separating rocks with different speeds (S_1, S_2) of wave propagation. For simplicity, (a) to (c) show individual wave paths, akin to rays of light. (a) Reflection and refraction of energy at a small angle of incidence, where the wave path in the lower, higher-speed rock is refracted towards the layer with lower wave speed. (b) The critical angle of incidence results in refraction along the boundary. (c) Incidence angles higher than the critical value result in strong reflection. (d) In this case energy from the seismic source is shown expanding outwards as a spherical wave front from its source at X. The diagram shows the change in position of this wave front over time. At point A, the incidence angle is at its critical value, and refracted energy travels along the boundary, to 'leak' out upwards (note this 'leakage' is at the critical angle too), eventually to reach the surface at Y. Because that part of the wave that has been refracted at the critical angle travels in the higher-speed lower layer, when some of its energy re-emerges by 'leakage' it has travelled further than that in the corresponding wave in the upper, slower layer. Beyond a certain distance from the source along the surface, the refracted wave reaches the surface before that part travelling directly in the slower layer. Note: the diagram shows only those wave fronts that reach the surface first.

2.2.1 Seismic refraction experiments

Figure 2.6d shows that the first wave fronts to arrive at detectors close to the source (X) are those that travel in the surface layer. However, waves refracted into the lower, faster layer to travel parallel to the boundary 'leak' energy across the boundary. This 'leaked' energy travels along wave paths at the critical angle to the boundary. Because waves travel faster below the boundary, eventually they catch up and overtake those travelling directly along the surface and become the first arrivals at geophones more distant from the source, despite the fact that they have to travel further to reach the surface. Figure 2.6d implies that plotting times of first arrival against distance along the surface should give information about both the depth to the boundary and the seismic-wave speeds (S_1 and S_2) of the two layers that it separates.

Figure 2.7 shows such a plot. The line from X to R shows the times at which direct waves travelling in the top layer of rock arrive at geophones. Waves that were refracted at the boundary plot on the line R to Y. The gradient of the line for refracted arrivals is lower than that for direct waves, because, having travelled part-way through the deeper layer with higher speed, they take less time to travel the same distance. The gradients of the two lines are inversely proportional to the wave-propagation speeds in the two corresponding layers; they are the *reciprocal* $(1/S)$ of these speeds. Calculating the depth to the boundary is a little more complicated. The values of time and distance for point R, where refracted waves overtake direct waves, must be governed by the extra distance travelled by refracted waves through the top layer, and by the difference between the two travel speeds. From the geometry in Figure 2.6d, the depth (d) to the boundary is given by:

$$d = \frac{t_0 S_1 S_2}{2\sqrt{S_2^2 - S_1^2}} \tag{2.1}$$

where t_0 is the intercept on the time axis by projecting the plot of refracted arrivals back beyond R, or:

$$d = \frac{x_d}{2}\sqrt{\frac{S_2 - S_1}{S_2 + S_1}} \tag{2.2}$$

where x_d is the distance of R from the source at X.

This and the use of the gradients on the plot to calculate seismic-wave speeds of different layers form the basis for interpreting the results from seismic refraction experiments. Of course, the crust may have several layers through which seismic waves travel at different speeds, and that complicates matters. The seismograms record (hopefully) different sets of waves emanating from refraction at several boundaries, not merely the first arrivals as in the two-layer case. The time–distance plots show several lines with different gradients, and we summarize the approach to that problem shortly.

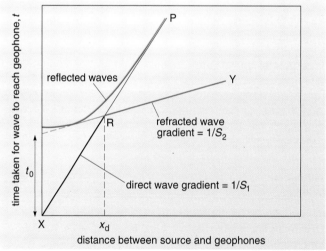

Figure 2.7 Plot of arrival time of seismic waves at the array of geophones laid out at increasing distances from the source (see Figure 2.6d). Point R, where the gradient of the plot changes, marks where seismic waves that have travelled in the lower layer of rock at higher speed overtake those travelling directly along the surface in the slower, upper layer.

Question 2.4 At what distance from an artificial source would refracted waves from the crust–mantle boundary (the Moho) become the first arrivals at geophones? How does that bear on the length of a survey line that seeks to discover the structure of the continental crust? Use seismic P-wave speeds for typical continental crust and mantle peridotite of 6.5 and 8.0 km s^{-1}, and a typical depth to the Moho of 35 km.

The answer to Question 2.4 implies that geophysicists face quite a challenge if they want to probe the seismic structure of the entire crust using seismic refraction. Each explosion needs 250 km of geophones laid out in a line. Since each experiment produces information relating to the whole crust underlying the line as an average, detail is at a premium, quite literally. More explosions and more shifts of the geophone line will give increasing detail, but there are two problems. The first is cost per experiment. The second should be obvious — the British Isles are densely populated. The problems associated with laying out a geophone line 250 km long, even once, are not insubstantial. The difficulties are worsened by the fact that generating enough energy to be detected 250 km away requires a disturbingly large explosion. The project must either drill deep holes or use existing mine workings, simply for safety. The largest such series of experiments in the British Isles — the Lithospheric Seismic Profile in Britain (LISPB) — used six sources, two in the sea off northern Scotland and four detonated in boreholes drilled for the purpose (Figure 2.8). Given good liaison, shorter refraction profiles are possible using quarry or mine blasts.

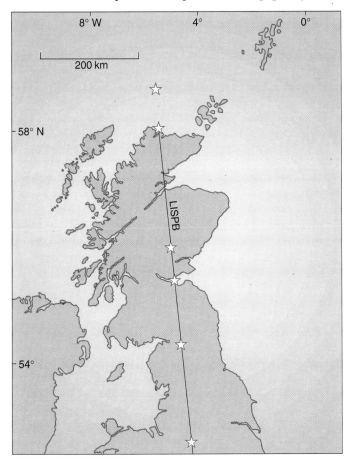

Figure 2.8 Line of the main seismic refraction profile conducted in the British Isles (LISPB = Lithospheric Seismic Profile in Britain). Shot points are shown as stars.

Deeply penetrating seismic refraction experiments produce as many segments on plots of arrival time against distance as there are crustal layers with distinct wave-propagation speeds. Often the differences are quite subtle, and on a simple time–distance graph like Figure 2.7 distinguishing them is a problem. One way of emphasizing the differences is to standardize the data by assuming that the upper layer propagates waves at a constant speed S_0, when the time axis plots $t - (x/S_0)$ where x is the distance between source and geophone. The effect of this is to change the sense of gradients in the plots. A layer which propagates waves at the same speed as the upper layer shows a horizontal plot; plots for faster layers have negative gradients; and those through which waves travel more slowly have positive gradients. You do not have to worry about these calculations.

Figure 2.9a shows all the seismograms from the geophone line used for the northernmost LISPB source on Figure 2.8. Notice that each seismogram shows subtle changes in the signal after energy first begins to arrive. The first step in interpretation is distinguishing between these changes, and correlating them between all the seismograms. That is a highly skilled task. The correlation lines are themselves standardized time against distance plots, based on an assumption of a 6 km s^{-1} speed in the uppermost layer.

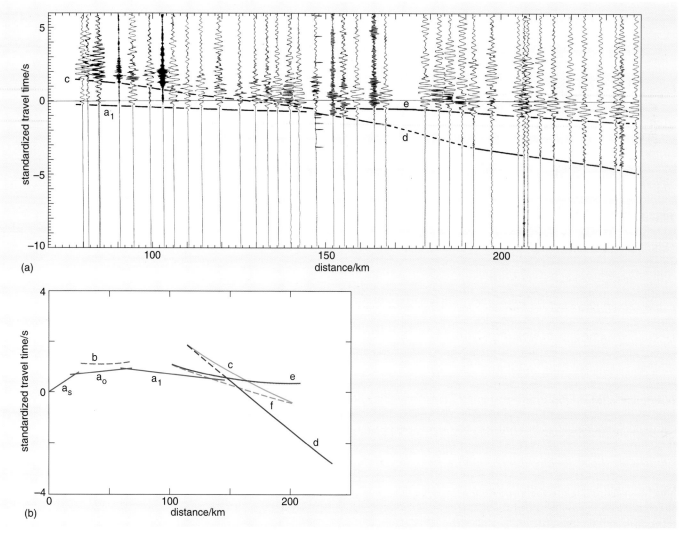

Figure 2.9 (a) Standardized travel time plotted against distance to the geophones laid out along the LISPB line for the northernmost source in Figure 2.8, fired off the north coast of Scotland. The lines a_1, c, d and e link arrivals of different signals on each of the seismograms. (b) Plots of standardized travel time against distance from the whole of the LISBP project. The uppermost layer is assumed to have a propagation speed (S_0) of 6.1 km s^{-1}.

- Which of the correlation lines on Figure 2.9a represents the upper crust underlying northern Scotland and which corresponds to the mantle beneath the Moho?

- Line a_1 starts at the source (standardized time 0, distance 0), is almost parallel to the distance axis, and so is close to 6 km s^{-1} (in fact it has a very gentle, negative slope, and this signifies a seismic-wave speed slightly higher than 6 km s^{-1}). The most distant lines (i.e. detected more than 140 km from the source, and likely to record data from deep levels) are e and d. Line d is steeper than e, and so represents a layer with a higher wave speed. Line d is likely to represent the sub-continental mantle with a seismic-wave speed of about 8 km s^{-1}.

The full LISPB data define eight lines (Figure 2.9b). After a great deal of processing and analysis based on the most probable crustal structure, guided by major structural boundaries known from surface mapping, the LISPB team compiled a schematic cross-section along the 700 km long profile, shown in Figure 2.10. Because the cost and social constraints on the experiment limited the project to only six sources, the section has low resolution, so the structure beneath several sections is unclear. Nonetheless, the LISPB experiment revealed some fundamental divisions in the British crust.

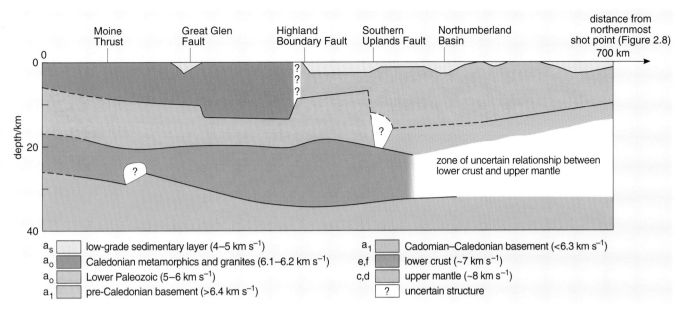

Figure 2.10 Schematic cross section of the British crust along the LISPB line, down to 40 km. Note that this is an interpretation from data that were acquired in only six segments (Figure 2.8), and many of the sharp boundaries are probably zones across which seismic-wave speed changes gradually. The letters in the key, such as a_s, e, and f, refer to the lines on Figure 2.9b.

The interpretation of LISPB in Figure 2.10 assumes a three-layer crust throughout the British Isles, whereas other interpretations suggest vertical transitions from one distinct crustal layer to the next. You should spend a few minutes studying Figure 2.10, and then attempt Question 2.5.

Question 2.5 (a) Is there any sign of a lateral change in the seismic-wave speed of the mantle or the lower crust beneath the British Isles? (b) What is the evidence for the major boundary in the upper crust beneath the Southern Uplands Fault? (c) Are there any other clearly demarcated boundaries?

Although somewhat sketchy, the LISPB data show that there is a fundamental, steep boundary in the middle and upper crust beneath northern Britain, which is associated with the Southern Uplands Fault. This fault shows extremely well on both the magnetic and Bouguer anomaly images of the British Isles (MAG and GRAV, Section 2.1), and must therefore extend to considerable depth in the crust. Similarly, the prominent Highland Boundary Fault also acts as a crustal boundary, separating seismically fast upper crustal metamorphic rocks of the Highlands from seismically slower Paleozoic sediments beneath the Scottish Midland Valley. You may think that an explanation for this lies in the Highland Boundary Fault being the southern boundary of the outcropping Dalradian metamorphic complex, and having a very large downthrow to the south. However, there is no seismic evidence that the Dalradian extends beneath the surface to the south of the Highland Boundary Fault. Below the Midland Valley, the mid-crustal layer is several kilometres thicker than beneath the Highlands, and so too is the deepest crustal layer. In fact, the Midland Valley is where the whole crust is at its thickest along the LISPB line, at about 35 km. Yet it also has a higher Bouguer gravity anomaly than do the Highlands (Activity 2.1). That can be explained by the thicker upper crust beneath the Dalradian of the southern Highlands, and the abundance of low-density granite intrusions there, and a thicker, denser mid-crustal layer beneath the Midland Valley. Carboniferous volcanic vents around the Firth of Forth are full of xenoliths of high-density granulites derived from the lower crust (Section 6.1).

● Do the LISPB data for the far north of Scotland conflict with geological evidence? (You may need to refer to Section 3.1 of Block 4.)

● Yes, they do. Figure 2.10 shows that the LISPB line crosses the Moine Thrust Zone, whose footwall has a thin, discontinuous cover of Torridonian and Cambro-Ordovician sediments resting on Pre-Caledonian basement — the Lewisian. On Figure 2.10, this basement is lumped with the Caledonian metamorphics and granites, leaving two deeper crustal layers approximately 18 and 23 km below the surface.

The nature of the two deeper crustal layers beneath northernmost Scotland is suggested by geological knowledge along the LISPB line. The northern outcrops of the Lewisian are upper crustal in origin and full of low-density granitic sheets, but further south the Lewisian is a granulite-facies complex, formed at deep crustal levels (Section 4 and Activity 4.1). These granulites possibly form the present mid-crustal layer that extends at least as far as the Great Glen Fault, but the deep crust remains an enigma.

Although coarse and poorly defined, the LISPB crustal section shows that the many structures resolved by gravity and magnetic data occur in three distinct seismic domains — the Scottish Highlands, the Midland Valley and the crust south of the Southern Uplands Fault. Resolving structural detail in the crust depends on seismic profiling that uses seismic reflection experiments.

2.2.2 Seismic reflection experiments

The reflective properties of geological boundaries are not only governed by differences between seismic-wave speeds, but by contrasts in the manner whereby they absorb energy. Materials that transmit seismic energy at different speeds do differ in this way, but so too do rocks that have the same speed. A boundary separating rocks with the same absorbing properties will not reflect much seismic energy. However, examining any stratigraphic sequence reveals a host of boundaries between quite different materials — shales, sandstones, limestones and so on. Each is a potential reflector, as would be a boundary between a sedimentary and an igneous rock, and the many compositional contrasts that metamorphic complexes contain. Reflection may even be encouraged by alignments of minerals in highly deformed rocks.

Using seismic-reflection data to reveal the depth to many such reflectors should reveal a variety of structures — dipping strata, folds, unconformities and displacements by faults, to name but a few. Seismic experiments record time but not depth, and as Figure 2.11a shows, the time is that taken for a reflected wave to travel down to a reflector and then back to the surface. For that reason, it is

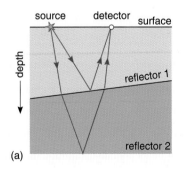

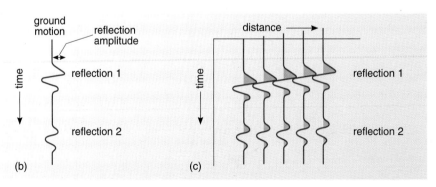

Figure 2.11 (a) Seismic wave paths associated with reflections by two boundaries separating rocks with different acoustic impedances. (b) The seismic trace from a single detector used in (a), time (the two-way time) increasing downwards and compressional arrivals being to the right. (c) Seismic traces from several detectors spread out from the source in (a) where the alignment of distinct reflection events shows the attitude of the reflecting boundary responsible — note that this is not true dip but distance against two-way time.

known as the **two-way time**. The average seismic-wave speed of the rocks through which the wave passes obviously plays a role in governing two-way time, as well as the actual distance travelled. Although geophysicists are able to convert two-way time to depth, we show the data in their two-way time form.

Seismic-reflection data are arranged so that two-way time increases downwards, the better to mimic a geological cross-section. Figure 2.11b shows a record from one detector in the set-up of Figure 2.11a, on which compressive arrivals deflect the trace rightwards. The earliest arrival is from the shallowest reflector. The traces from several detectors mimic the inclination of the reflectors (Figure 2.11c). In practice, geophysicists build up seismic reflection profiles by using many sources arranged along the desired line, each recorded by a string of detectors. The seismic reflection profiles that we use to show the crustal structure beneath the British Isles consist of reflectors drawn by experienced interpreters.

It is much cheaper to deploy seismic reflection surveys offshore rather than on land, and marine surveys avoid traffic noise, and can use far more energetic sources than would be tolerated onshore. Figure 2.12 shows the lines of offshore experiments conducted during the 1980s. Many of these were directed at segments of crust on which Mesozoic and Cenozoic sedimentary basins formed; hardly surprising as the researchers were supported by the oil industry. Others (DRUM and MOIST) focused on crustal structure across the Moine Thrust Zone. You will consider only three groups of profiles. The WINCH experiment between the Inner Hebrides and the Isle of Man, and the NEC profile close to shore in the North Sea and between Dundee and Whitby are parallel to the LISPB refraction profile, and cover the gross transition in crustal structure across the Southern Uplands. The other, from the SWAT experiment, covers crustal features that show up in the potential-field data over southern Britain. (*Note:* Many of the lines of seismic reflection experiments are shown on the Tectonic Map, where you can more easily relate them to the major geological features that they cross.)

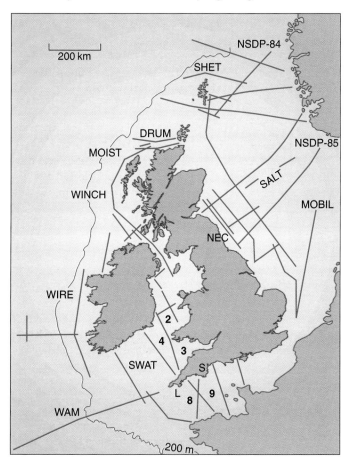

Figure 2.12   Deeply penetrating seismic reflection profiles conducted around the British Isles by the BIRPS (British Institutions' Reflection Profiling Syndicate) consortium. Each was designed to record reflections with two-way times of 15 seconds or more, sufficient to penetrate the continental crust. The three which you will be examining are that part of WINCH (Western Isles, North Channel) from the Inner Hebrides to the Isle of Man, the North East Coast (NEC), and one of the lines from South West Approaches Traverse (SWAT) that runs from the Irish Sea off Anglesey to the coast of North Cornwall. Those numbered are shown in Figure 2.14.

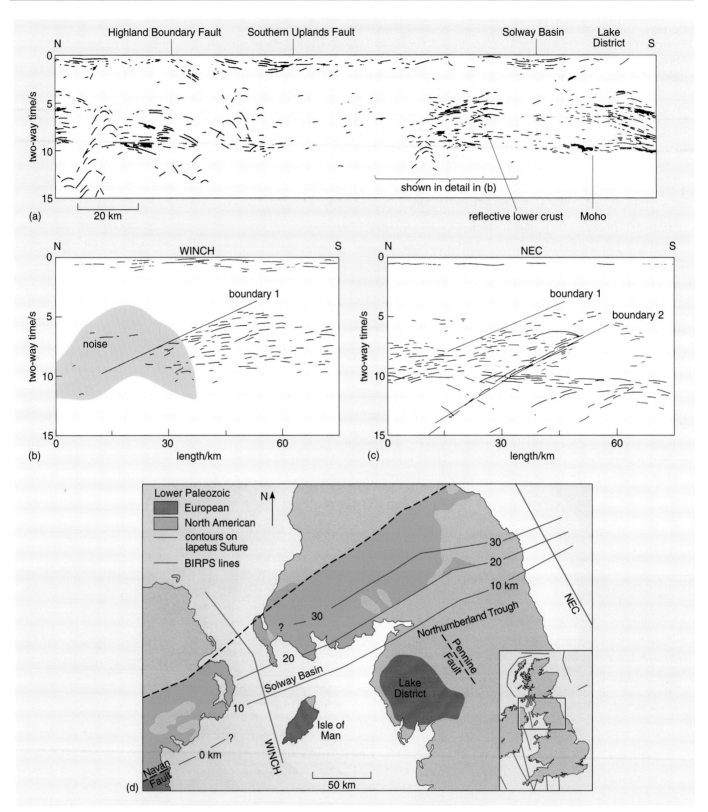

Figure 2.13 (a) Line drawing of reflecting boundaries that show in the WINCH reflection seismic profile from Islay in the north to the Irish Sea opposite the Lake District in the south. (b) Detail from the WINCH profile north of the Solway Basin. (c) Detail from that part of the NEC profile that approximately matches (b), along the regional strike. (d) Depth contours to a change in geo-electrical properties of the crust beneath Northern England and Southern Scotland.

Interpretations of the full WINCH data in Figure 2.13a show structures as deep as 15 seconds two-way time (equivalent to about 50 km below the surface) in the north, although in fact these are artefacts from data processing. To the south of the Highland Boundary Fault, there is little structure below about 10 seconds two-way time. This transition from structurally rich to almost blank data marks the Moho, and the crust is around 30 km thick — as predicted by LISPB for this segment.

- Potential-field and the LISPB seismic refraction data point strongly to a major boundary in crustal structure along the line of the Southern Uplands Fault. Do clear features on the WINCH data confirm that?

- No they do not, there being few linear features that would indicate some steep zone of displacement or contrast. Incidentally, despite the magnitude of downthrow on the Highland Boundary Fault, that too has no discernible signature on the seismic reflection data.

Despite persuasive geophysical evidence for the tectonic significance of the Southern Uplands Fault, it seems not to be so profound on the corresponding reflection profile. This is because steeply dipping faults are not easily detected by seismic reflection, except where they can clearly be seen to displace low-angle reflectors; there are few of those in the vicinity of both major faults.

- Where to the south of the Southern Uplands Fault on the WINCH profile *are* there signs of major structures in the deep crust? Is there any sign of dipping reflectors, and if so, what is their direction of dip?

- To the north of the Solway Basin, beneath the southern part of the Southern Uplands, there are many reflectors between 5–10 seconds two-way time. Some of them dip northwards, but there are also many flat-lying reflectors in the deep crust, which extend southwards to the projected position of the Lake District. All the reflectors peter out to the north.

Figure 2.13b shows more detail in the WINCH profile for the area just north of the Solway Basin, and Figure 2.13c shows detail from the NEC profile for a nearly parallel section that is approximately 200 km along the regional strike to the north-east.

> Question 2.6 Compare Figure 2.13b and c. (a) What feature(s) do both parts have in common? Describe any features that show a distinct dip. (b) Describe the main features that show in Figure 2.13c.

Because two independent seismic profiles separated by 200 km show much the same north-dipping feature in the deep crust, that feature is almost certainly real. It must represent a major geological structure that has no clear manifestation at the surface. To check, and to add information about the crust beneath the Southern Uplands, Simon Klemperer and Drummond Matthews of the BIRPS consortium conducted a geo-electrical survey of the crust on land (Figure 2.13d). The details of that method are beyond this Course, but the survey reveals changes in electrical properties in the deep crust, and defines a boundary where that change takes place. It too dips northwards, at approximately the same angle as the seismic-reflection boundaries, and lies in approximately the same geographic position. Projecting the contours on the electrical anomaly in the crust to the present surface suggests that it might outcrop in the northern Lake District. At that position there is no clear feature, such as a major lithological boundary, to suggest what the deep structure is, although across the Irish Sea the Navan Fault does lie in approximately the right position.

The key to understanding the significance of the crust-wide zone that dips northwards is neither geophysical nor lithological, but paleontological. The Lower Paleozoic sedimentary rocks of the Lake District and Southern Uplands, which occur on opposite sides of the zone, contain different fossil assemblages. To the north, the faunas are similar to those found in North America. Faunas to the south have affinities with those of the rest of Europe. During the late 1960s, this sharp faunal boundary was the main evidence for two separate fragments of old crust that merged in the Silurian to form most of the British Isles. The faunal differences suggested that, before the Silurian, those fragments must have been separated by an ocean wide enough to prevent mingling of marine animals and their larvae. Later, this conjecture found support from the quite different paleomagnetic pole positions revealed by the now adjacent Cambrian and Ordovician rocks. The geophysical evidence for a major structural boundary emerged only in the 1980s.

● In order for the two provinces now to lie next to each other, what process might have been involved?

○ The oceanic lithosphere that formerly separated them must have been consumed by subduction, in order for the crustal fragments to join by collision at a tectonic suture.

This implies that the most probable explanation for the north-dipping geophysical features is that they represent a suture zone (Block 4). The dip suggests that the deep crust beneath the Southern Uplands may preserve a relic of the subduction zone itself.

That ocean between the two Lower Paleozoic faunal provinces and once-independent crustal fragments became referred to as the **Iapetus Ocean**, after a minor figure in Greek mythology (Iapetus was one of 3000 ocean nymphs born to Oceanus and Tethys — both Titans, as well you might imagine). The line along which it finally closed by collision of the separate continents is the **Iapetus Suture**; the zone between the Lake District and the Southern Uplands Fault. The Iapetus Suture, unlike the Tethyan Suture (Block 4), is not obvious, for three reasons: the way in which collision incorporated many small terranes in the suture zone; the profound structural modifications that resulted from collision; and its blanketing by thick Silurian sediments shortly after it formed. And, of course, much of the area has little outcropping rock. The Iapetus story picks up again in Section 5, where you will examine evidence for the processes involved.

The NE–SW strike of bedding in the Lower Paleozoic rocks of the Midlands and Wales contrasts strongly with the mainly E–W strike of Upper Paleozoic rocks (Devonian and Carboniferous) in Devon and Cornwall (Figure 2.5). Your work with the potential-field data for the British Isles (Activity 2.1) showed that most clearly on GRAV. Only a few E–W features in SW England showed up on MAG. The line that roughly separates these structural provinces is the northern boundary of intense deformation that took place throughout much of central to southern Europe after the Carboniferous, during an orogenic event known variously as the Amorican, Variscan or Hercynian (depending on when and where immediately post-Carboniferous deformation took place). That boundary is known in the British Isles as the **Variscan Front**.

No deep seismic refraction survey like LISPB crosses southern Britain. The offshore SWAT seismic reflection experiments (Figure 2.12) were aimed primarily at investigating the Mesozoic to Cenozoic sedimentary basins of the Western Approaches shown on the Tectonic Map. The lines run at high angles to the structural trends both north and south of the Variscan Front to seek possible controls over the basins by major structures in the older rocks beneath them. Reflections from beneath the sedimentary basins outline the overall crustal structures (Figure 2.14). All the SWAT lines show on the Tectonic Map, so that you can see how they relate to broad surface geology and structures inferred from them.

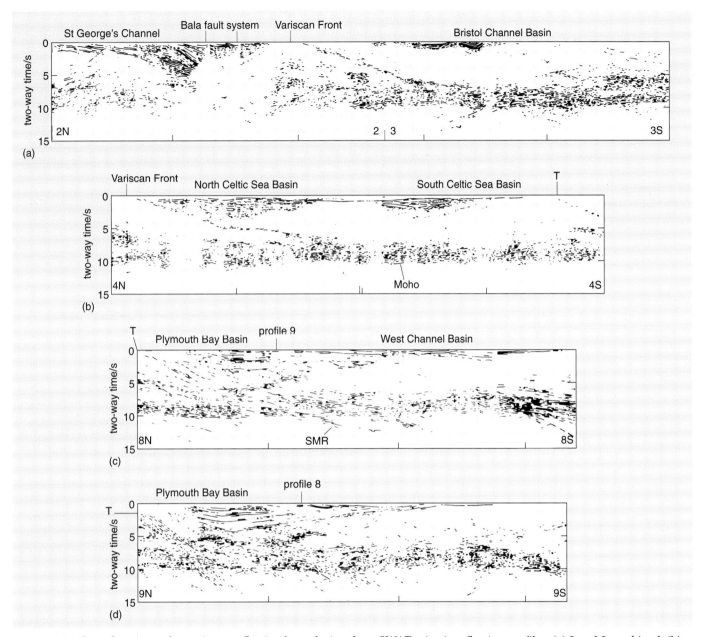

Figure 2.14 Line drawings of prominent reflecting boundaries along SWAT seismic-reflection profiles: (a) 2 and 3 combined; (b) 4; (c) 8; and (d) 9 (see Figure 2.12 for their locations). SMR sub-Moho reflections; T possible thrusts. (a) and (b) show approximate position of the Variscan Front projected onto the line of section from surface geology in South Wales and the Irish Republic respectively.

Question 2.7 Examine the profiles shown in Figure 2.14a and b. Are there any signs in the profiles of features that might represent structures related to the Variscan Front? If so, describe them briefly in terms of their attitude and in relation to the Moho (as in Figure 2.13, the Moho lies at about 10 seconds two-way time, beneath the prominent reflectors in the lower crust).

Your answer to Question 2.7 should reveal that the structure related to the Variscan Front is almost crust-wide, but it shows no sign of displacing either the deep-crustal zone of densely packed reflectors or the Moho. Instead, it seems to merge with the first. Its change in dip on Figure 2.14b marks a change from an upper crustal ramp to a flat in the middle crust, which might indicate that a mid-crustal décollement operated during its evolution.

● From the evidence on the Tectonic Map for the sense of movement in the near-surface strata, what kind of fault does the structure that is related to the Variscan Front represent?

● In South Wales, the Upper and Lower Paleozoic strata define large-scale anticlines and synclines, indicative of Variscan compression. The structure probably represents a major thrust.

The density of reflectors in the lower crust increases to the south of the point where the Variscan Front thrust joins them. This may indicate that intense ductile deformation in the lower crust distributed the movement on the thrust through a large volume of rocks at high temperatures and pressures (temperatures will be greater than 600 °C in the deep crust). Because the structure seems not to have affected the Moho, and does not separate different mid- and lower crust, unlike the Iapetus Suture, it is unlikely to represent a plate boundary. More likely it was the lower boundary to considerable thickening of the southern part of the British crust. To accommodate the great thickness of Devonian and Carboniferous marine sediments in Devon and Cornwall, the crust may have been thinned by earlier extension. The tendency of thinned crust to be thickened later, when extensional tectonics give way to compression, is a common feature of many orogenic belts, and is an example of basin inversion (Block 4, Section 2.4). Incidentally, if you look at the extensional faults affecting the Younger Cover (shown in green on the Tectonic Map) to the east of Devon and Cornwall, you will find that they are parallel to brown Variscan thrust faults. The area underwent further tectonic inversion during the Mesozoic and Cenozoic, to become an extensional regime, when Variscan thrusts helped control normal faulting. At the time the Alps began to form in the early Cenozoic, these normal faults were inverted to take up compressional deformation that resulted in the broad Cenozoic anticlines and synclines that affect the Younger Cover of southern England.

Profiles 8 and 9 (Figure 2.14c, d) both end in the north close to the line joining the Lizard (L) and Start Point (Figure 2.12). Those locations each reveal high-grade metamorphic rocks and, in the case of the Lizard, a possible ophiolite thrust northwards over the deformed sedimentary rocks of Upper Paleozoic age (Section 5.5). That thrust is marked by a 'T' at the north end of both profiles. Quite plainly, the thrust on both sections lines up with dipping zones of reflectors.

● In what ways do the dipping zones of reflectors that probably link to the Lizard–Start Point thrust differ from those associated with the Variscan Front (Figure 2.14a and b)?

● They are wider and steeper. There are also signs that they continue through the lower crust and link with reflectors that penetrate for about three seconds two-way time into the mantle. They bear some resemblance to the seismic-reflection 'signature' of the Iapetus Suture, but unlike it, do not separate crustal segments with differing seismic response.

The Lizard–Start Point thrust is crust-wide and penetrates the mantle. You will recall from GRAV (Activity 2.1) that that there is a prominent gravity high trending eastwards from Cornwall, just to the south of the outcropping thrust. This is despite the thick, low-density sediments of the Plymouth Bay Basin over which the gravity high passes. The most reasonable interpretation is that the high is due to slabs of high-density mafic to ultramafic rock along the thrust, one of which outcrops as the Lizard ophiolite (dark green on the Tectonic Map). We return to the significance of this feature in Section 5.

2.2.3 Summary of Section 2.2

- Given sufficient energy input, both seismic refraction and reflection experiments provide information on deep crustal structure. Refraction data help subdivide the gross layered structure of the crust in terms of the speed at which seismic waves travel through different layers. Those from seismic reflection profiles show in greater detail the attitude of boundaries that separate rocks with subtly different properties. Reflection profiles give information on crustal structure, such as large-scale flexures, unconformities and low-angled faults. High-angle faults are only detectable where they displace recognizable 'packages' of low-angled reflectors.

- The profile from the onshore LISPB seismic refraction experiment revealed major changes in gross crustal structure across the Highland Boundary and Southern Uplands Faults. The crust beneath the Scottish Midland Valley is the thickest in the British Isles, and it shows higher gravitational potential than do the Highlands, so it is also denser. The lower gravity anomaly over the Dalradian metamorphic complex is probably due to a combination of a thicker upper crust to the north of the Highland Boundary Fault and the large number of granitic plutons that intruded the Dalradian. To the south of the Southern Uplands Fault, the distinction between upper and lower continental crust breaks down, and compared with the crust beneath the Midland Valley, wave speeds are generally lower.

- Seismic reflection profiles from the WINCH and NEC experiments reveal no clear features that coincide with the Highland Boundary and Southern Uplands Faults. However, NEC in particular revealed a zone of northward-dipping reflectors that descend beneath the Southern Uplands from a line joining north Northumbria and the Solway. This coincides with a major boundary between Cambrian and Ordovician fossil faunas, that had been suggested previously to mark the line of closure of an ocean at that time (Iapetus). Most Earth scientists now regard this feature as a remnant of the subduction zone involved in the Iapetus Suture.

- The Variscan Front of southern Britain marks the northern limit of intense deformation to the south at the end of the Carboniferous Period. Seismic reflection profiles at right angles to it do show several large thrust faults to its south, but no evidence for a profound difference in crustal structure. So the Variscan Front is not a suture separating two former lithospheric plates. A thrust revealed by profiles across the southern part of Devon and Cornwall does seem to cross the Moho. Its projection to the surface coincides with high-grade metamorphic rocks and a possible ophiolite. This thrust is possibly a Variscan terrane boundary.

2.3 A tripartite alliance

From your analysis of potential-field and seismic data, you should have reached the broad conclusion that the lithosphere beneath the British Isles comprises three distinct blocks, separated by two fundamental structures (see inset map at top left of the Tectonic Map). The Mesozoic to Recent Younger Cover forms a veneer over this tripartite division, as does the Upper Paleozoic, Older Cover for the northern two masses. The first-order structures are the hidden line of the Iapetus Suture roughly trending from Newcastle through Carlisle towards the Shannon estuary, and the Variscan Front that shows at the surface in southernmost Ireland and South Wales and trends through Kent into the Low Countries beneath later sediments. The northernmost block contains crystalline and/or highly deformed basement rocks that range in age from about 3000 to

400 Ma. That between the Iapetus Suture and the Variscan Front has outcrops of basement with an age range between about 650 to 400 Ma. The Variscan orogenic belt is dominantly composed at the surface of deformed Devonian to Carboniferous rocks with small outcrops of Precambrian basement at its southern limit in the British Isles.

This division is almost certainly real, and its profound nature is confirmed by the separation of very different Lower Paleozoic fossil associations north and south of the Iapetus Suture that suggests the former presence of an extensive ocean. That across the Variscan Front is not so profound, except in terms of upper-crustal deformation and sedimentary facies in the Upper Paleozoic rocks. The Variscan Front separates sediments laid down to the north during fluctuations between terrestrial and shallow-marine shelf environments from deeper marine sediments (mainly turbidites) to the south. A suture related to Variscan events occurs to the south of the British Isles, and represents the closure of the so-called Rheic Ocean that separated it from what is now Africa. However, Britain's tectonic architecture is much more complicated in detail. The synoptic map at top left of the Tectonic Map shows as many as a dozen terranes that geologists have recognized, many of which are small slivers. In Section 5, you will examine evidence that allowed Earth scientists to separate them and to evaluate how they formed and how they became 'shuffled' together.

The greatest uncertainty concerns the nature of the deep crust beneath these three segments, for it is completely hidden, except in the north-west of Scotland in the footwall of the Moine Thrust Zone (Block 4). There, crystalline basement of the Archean (>2500 Ma) Lewisian Complex (Section 4) shows clear evidence of having formed the lower and middle part of the earliest vestige of British crust. It is tempting to project that ancient infrastructure beneath the northern block, but, apart from thrust slices of possibly Lewisian crust in the most northerly parts of the Caledonian orogen, there is not a shred of direct evidence for that conjecture. The only support is from similar seismic-wave speeds from the two deepest layers on the LISPB profile (Figure 2.9). The deep crust beneath northern and central England, and Wales is clearly different seismically; indeed it is difficult to resolve its deepest parts. Earth scientists assume it to be the product of much younger Precambrian crust-forming events, from the ~600 Ma age of sparsely outcropping rocks in the Midlands and North Wales. However, GRAV and MAG show features that cannot be explained by the Older and Younger Cover, nor by the NE–SW trend of Caledonian structures. They suggest that at the heart of the English Midlands is a buried block of Precambrian crust. This, together with similar features in the Netherlands and Belgium, helps explain the stability of this area during both the Lower and Upper Paleozoic, when thin marine-shelf and thin terrestrial sediments respectively were deposited on the block.

In Section 3, we step out to the global context of the last billion years of geological evolution, so that you might better understand Britain's own development. The starting frame of reference is the Pangaea supercontinent that finally assembled around the time of the Variscan orogeny, some 290 Ma ago, as did the British lithosphere.

Objectives for Section 2

Now that you have completed this Section, you should be able to:

2.1   Understand the meaning of all the terms printed in **bold**.

2.2   Use images of gravitational and magnetic potential fields, in conjunction with regional geological maps, to recognize areas of thick sedimentary cover, large bodies of igneous rocks, and major structural and igneous features in basement rocks that are either hidden by sedimentary cover, or exposed at the surface.

2.3   Distinguish between those aspects of crustal structure which seismic refraction and seismic reflection data can reveal.

2.4   Recognize major faults on line drawings of seismic reflection profiles.

Now try the following questions to check your understanding of Section 2.

Question 2.8   Use the Tectonic Map, GRAV and MAG to discuss the large features shown around: (a) 53° N, 4° W; (b) 52° 50′ N, 2° 40′ W; (c) 51° 40′ to 53° N, 2° 20′ to 4° W.

Question 2.9   What geophysical and geological features in Britain help define the Iapetus Suture and the possible plate boundary associated with the Variscan Orogeny?

3 Great events: a global context for the evolution of the British Isles

Geology in the British Isles is complicated and interesting because it is the product of tectonic process that acted on three distinct blocks, which aggregated between about 400 and 300 Ma ago. Essentially, the British Isles' lithosphere is only different from that of much larger continental masses because it expresses so much in miniature. It grew in broadly the same ways that formed western North America (Block 1, Section 1.4.3), and which destine the island arcs of the West Pacific to join Eurasia (Block 1, Activities 1.1 and 1.2). Its growth involved processes at constructive, destructive and conservative margins, and grasping these processes needs the broadest possible context. In this Section, we review evidence for global tectonic evolution as far back in time as the evidence permits, and how it influenced all continental material.

At present, continental lithosphere is scattered piecemeal across the face of the planet following the break-up of the **Pangaea** supercontinent that had stabilized by the Permian. Since the start of the Mesozoic Era, the British Isles have been a passive and tiny part of Pangaea's largest fragment, Eurasia, with the exception of episodes of extension that formed sedimentary basins around British shores, and included major igneous events that affected central and NW Scotland at about 320 and 60 Ma ago (Section 6). Most of the British Isles' infrastructure is the product of great events that took place before the Devonian Period 400 Ma ago, and before Pangaea came into being.

Our treatment of the British Isles' global context looks mainly at tectonic processes that extend back to those which operated 2500 Ma ago. We do this by progressively moving back in geological time from well-known to increasingly uncertain configurations of continents. Various lines of evidence help to reconstruct the changing global scene of continental positions and inferred oceanic plate margins. Where possible, you will track those two main components of the British Isles that the Iapetus Suture separates: to the north, Scotland and northernmost Ireland; and England, Wales and the rest of Ireland to the south. However, your attention will focus on global processes affecting all the continents. We do not expect you to remember precise reconstructions of continental masses and oceans, or the timings of continental amalgamation and fragmentation. It is more important that you should understand the evidence that enabled geologists to trace the sequence of events that ultimately united the British lithosphere.

3.1 The break-up of Pangaea

About 250 Ma ago, at the end of the Permian Period and the Paleozoic Era, most continental crust had become clumped together in the supercontinent Pangaea, through continent–continent collisions during the previous 150 Ma. Later in this Section, we will return to those epochal events and others that preceded them, for it was they that assembled the British Isles' crustal infrastructure as we know it now.

During the Permian, the British Isles lay near the centre of Pangaea, and throughout the Mesozoic Era its relief slowly subsided through erosion. Periodic inundation of the British Isles by shallow seas during long-term extensional processes laid down a sedimentary veneer of Younger Cover. Variations in the thickness of these sediments define several depositional basins. The British Isles' tectonic quiescence during the Mesozoic stemmed from its remoteness from the main sites where Pangaea's break-up resulted in collisional orogenies.

Activity 3.1

This Activity concerns plate motions and the break-up of Pangaea, and uses an animation of the positions of modern continents at various times during the Mesozoic Era. It should take you about 30 minutes to complete this Activity.

Between 60 and 55 Ma, the British Isles experienced their last major geological events with a direct connection to plate tectonics. Partial melting in the mantle, which eventually added basaltic magma to what became the mid-Atlantic Ridge, occurred beneath north-western Britain in the Paleocene. Major volcanoes and fissures erupted mafic lavas to flood what are now Northern Ireland and the Hebrides, as part of the North Atlantic Tertiary Igneous Province. We return to these events in Section 6.

3.2 Before Pangaea

In reading this Section, you should bear in mind that the further back in time geological investigations go, the less certain are the ideas that research helps to develop. The material that we present here is abbreviated, and the figures express the views of a limited number of geologists; no consensus exists at present, except that large continent-bearing plates did assemble and break up. The vast scope of pre-Pangaea events, both in time and across the whole continental surface, has resulted in quite meagre pickings as regards hard facts. New work from previously unstudied places and times frequently results in collective head-scratching by those bold enough to erect all-encompassing theories for long-past events. This holds just as much for the tiny contribution of exposures in the British Isles as it does for the global picture.

Paleomagnetic data for the period after 144 Ma, which coincide with plate reconstructions based on other grounds, suggest that paleopole information can assist in reconstruction of continental positions for earlier periods. There are two conditions, however:

1 that paleopoles are known for all continental segments for any particular time in the past;

2 that there are recognizable means of linking what were once juxtaposed continental segments, such as orogenic belts that share a common age and that can be aligned across a suspected former boundary between segments.

A reconstruction of Pangaea at 250 Ma ago (Figure 3.1) illustrates these conditions. Plotting the relative positions of modern continents for that time depended on paleopoles of that age falling in the same polar position, and several orogenic belts older than 250 Ma do continue across the joins.

⬤ In Figure 3.1, what is the evidence based on alignment of old orogens that helps 'tie' (a) North America and northern Europe, and (b) South America and Africa?

⬤ (a) The reconstruction of the North Atlantic region lines up parts of an orogenic belt that is between 500 and 400 Ma old — the Caledonian belt, plus two either side of it that are about 1100 Ma and 300 Ma old. (b) South America and west Africa share a complex system of orogenic belts dated at around 650–550 Ma, and also an area of rocks that are much older — the last is a craton dating back to more than 2500 Ma.

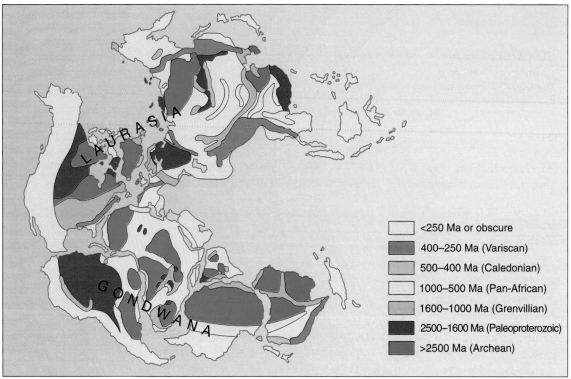

Figure 3.1   Pangaea at the end of the Paleozoic (250 Ma ago). Orogenic belts of different ages that pre-date the assembly of Pangaea are shown on each of its segments. *Notes:* The map shows outlines of modern continents for ease of recognition, and parts of these formed after the accretion of Pangaea. Compiled from many sources, many of which conflict in their interpretation, this is not a definitive map, and other interpretations for parts of Pangaea appear in Figures 3.2 and 3.3.

There are other examples of orogenic belts that cross the re-united margins of modern continents which you could have cited. Another important feature is the alignment of igneous dyke swarms that may have formed when modern continental margins originated by rifting at the start of the present round of sea-floor spreading.

The crucial point to glean from Figure 3.1 is that each of the pre-Permian orogenic belts represents collision between continental segments of greater antiquity. These orogens are akin to the Alpine-Himalayan belt formed by Africa–Europe and India–Asia collisions during the Cenozoic. Block 4 covered the processes and the igneous and metamorphic products related to such continent–continent collisions. That is not to assume, however, that all conformed to the basically head-on processes involved in the Cenozoic examples.

Some of these pre-Pangaea orogenic belts, such as the Urals, represent the lines along which Pangaea's components met, but others are far older. Those between 250 and 500 Ma old are literally the sutures of Pangaea — where it became 'stitched together' as a result of continental plate movements. It is safe to assume, in a general sense, that such sutures represent the graveyards of oceans that once separated the continental segments of Pangaea. For collision to have taken place, the lithosphere beneath those oceans must have descended into the mantle by subduction. Indeed, many orogenic belts contain fragments of such oceanic lithosphere that escaped subduction, in the form of ophiolite complexes. Subduction of oceanic lithosphere also generates new crust by partial melting above Wadati–Benioff zones, either in oceanic island arcs like those presently decorating the West Pacific (Block 1) or at active continental margins such as the Andes (Block 3). Sutures frequently preserve evidence for the accretion of volcanic arcs, which form predominantly magmatic terranes. Once again, a good example comes from the India–Asia collision zone of Cenozoic times, in the form of the Kohistan Terrane of NW Pakistan (Block 4).

Activity 3.2

This Activity examines plate motions between 400 and 250 Ma, and uses an animation that reconstructs the assembly of Pangaea during the Upper Paleozoic Era. This Activity should take you about 30 minutes.

The collage of orogenic belts and intervening, older crustal blocks that made up Pangaea depicts the way the world had become at the time when tectonics welded together the three or four tiny segments of the British Isles. Our geology is a microcosm of a much larger mass of northern Pangaea, or **Laurasia**.

Shift your focus now to the southern half of Pangaea on Figure 3.1, to **Gondwana**, noting that there are more age divisions of Precambrian orogenic belts than shown on Figure 1.2, Block 4.

- How does evidence for Phanerozoic orogenic activity relate to the tectonic collage that makes up Gondwana? What might your observations signify as regards its assembly?

- Orogenic belts younger than 500 Ma are found only at the margins of this half of Pangaea. This suggests that the assembly of Gondwana pre-dates events such as the Caledonian (500–400 Ma) and Variscan (400–300 Ma) orogenies. Gondwana was a supercontinent in its own right through the early part of the Phanerozoic.

The alignment of post-500 Ma orogenic belts around Gondwana suggests three things. First, the connections between such belts in today's southern Andes, the southern fringe of South Africa, West Antarctica and what is now eastern Australia helps confirm the goodness of fit of the Pangaea reconstruction. Secondly, their peripheral position suggests that none of them is likely to represent continent–continent collision. Instead, they must be products of destructive plate margins on the flanks of great oceans that existed throughout the early Phanerozoic. Thirdly, and this stems from the second conjecture, the Andean–West Antarctic–East Australian belt probably contains more completely new continental crust than older crust accreted as microcontinental slivers. It is probably dominated by the products of evolving magmas formed at subduction zones — perhaps accreted island arcs and continental-margin magmatism — plus sediments eroded from the ancient internal zones of the orogen. The Andes, West Antarctica and Eastern Australia therefore contribute nothing to tectonic reconstructions for Precambrian times.

- When did Gondwana probably assemble?

- Gondwana consists of several cratons that formed more than a billion years ago. These are separated by large orogenic belts whose ages range from about 1000 to 550 Ma old. The largest of them formed between 650 to 550 Ma ago. One swings through NW Africa and Brazil to link with lesser belts wrapping around the Kalahari craton. Another extends from modern Arabia through East Africa to East Antarctica. The bulk of Gondwana therefore came together by collision between its component cratons around 650 to 550 Ma ago.

There are other features that suggest an earlier clumping of cratons in Gondwana.

- Can you suggest which of the Gondwana cratons had assembled before the great events of 650–550 Ma?

- Eastern India and East Antarctica are separated on Figure 3.1 by an orogen dated between 1600 and 1000 Ma, that extends into and divides Australia. In fact, this orogen formed between 1100 and 1000 Ma.

The 1100 to 1000 Ma age also occurs as a fringe wrapping the Kalahari craton and what is now the western flank of the Amazonia craton. There are signs of even earlier orogenic episodes in Gondwana, but we have left them off Figure 3.1 for simplicity.

3.2.1   The mother of all continents — Rodinia

Taking a broader look at the whole of Pangaea reveals that the 1100 Ma time-frame crops up in many other places. The largest of these orogens extends through Laurasia from Texas, to the west of the Caledonian and Variscan belts of eastern North America, through Labrador to link with evidence of an 1100-Ma-old orogeny in East Greenland and southern Scandinavia.

On the evidence of age alone, orogeny seems to have been global around 1100 Ma ago. The first place where these events were described was in eastern Canada, around the little town of Grenville. The orogeny around 1100 Ma is widely known as the **Grenvillian**. A common time of origin is not the only thing that links Grenvillian belts worldwide. As well as comprising highly deformed and metamorphosed rocks, the Grenvillian orogens are vast repositories of a peculiar igneous rock type known as anorthosite, composed almost entirely of calcium-rich feldspar. Similar rocks do crop up later in geological history, but only in minor amounts. The Grenvillian anorthosites span a period of around 250 Ma, which suggests that the mantle continually supplied the anorthosites' parent magma during regional extension, until the widespread period of collision at 1100 Ma. Much the same features characterize the 1100 Ma belt that separates India and East Antarctica in Gondwana, and in Madagascar.

As well as being global, the 1100-Ma-old orogens' huge volumes of peculiar magmatic rocks points to some unique event in the mantle around 1400 to 1100 Ma ago. The haphazard distribution of Grenvillian orogens on Figure 3.1 is the product of at least three rounds of later plate movements and clumping of continental masses. Explaining their global occurrence became a compelling issue for some geologists in the late 1980s. They used two sorts of clue: paleomagnetic pole positions from continental fragments of Grenvillian age; and the trends of orogenic belts of that and older ages. Since the quest to resolve the Grenvillian began, geophysicists have deciphered many more poles of different ages for different continental segments, with improved precision. We shall come to the use of high-quality paleomagnetic data shortly. The first hold used by those grappling to push continental reconstruction to four times the age of Pangaea focused on splicing together Grenvillian orogenic belts in different segments of ancient crust, much as Alfred Wegener used traces of orogens on either side of the Atlantic to support his reconstruction of Pangaea.

Figure 3.2 shows the trends of orogenic belts in North America, including those that are older than 1400 Ma. You should note that, although the trends are clear for the eastern parts and for the Canadian Shield, a great deal of western North America is blanketed by sediments that are younger than the last orogenic events there. Also, the strip down the modern Pacific coast as far as the eastern edge of the Rocky Mountains has been deformed by several orogens since 250 Ma ago, most of which involved the accretion of terranes formed during the evolution of the East Pacific oceanic lithosphere (Block 1, Section 1.4.3). Precambrian rocks do outcrop in these partly hidden or reworked areas.

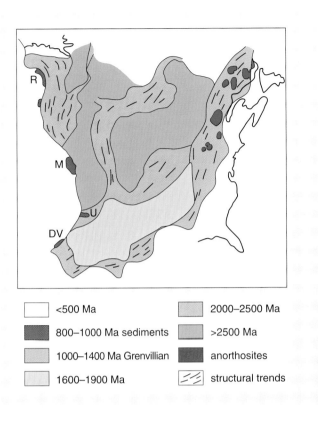

Figure 3.2   Trends of Paleozoic and Precambrian orogenic belts in North America. The Precambrian orogenic belts are reconstructed from continuous exposures of highly deformed and metamorphosed rocks in the Canadian Shield, plus isolated occurrences of Precambrian rocks where younger sedimentary cover has been removed by erosion, with evidence drawn from trends in the magnetic-field and gravity maps of North America. Sedimentary rocks that are dominated by turbidites with interbedded lava flows ranging from 800–1000 Ma outcrop at DV (Death Valley), M (Montana), R (Racklan, Alaska), and U (Uinta Mountains), Nevada.

Legend:
- <500 Ma
- 800–1000 Ma sediments
- 1000–1400 Ma Grenvillian
- 1600–1900 Ma
- 2000–2500 Ma
- >2500 Ma
- anorthosites
- structural trends

Question 3.1   Assuming that the trends shown on Figure 3.2 are real, describe briefly the Precambrian features at the western limit of geological information in North America.

The features that you should have seen are reminiscent of the geology of the west coast of Africa and the east coast of South America in their present positions, i.e. abrupt truncations of old orogens that typify lines of continental break-up. What draws further attention to the western margin of North America is that the line of truncation has patchy occurrences of lightly metamorphosed sediments formed at the end of and after the Grenvillian. The first geologists to attempt an explanation were Eldridge Moores of the University of California and Ian Dalziel of the University of Texas. In 1991, Moores discovered that other geologists had suggested similarities in age and mode of formation for roughly 800 Ma sedimentary rocks in both western Canada and eastern Australia, that might imply a link between North America and that part of Gondwana. Sharing this knowledge, Dalziel and Moores each speculated that the missing half of the truncated margin of North America might lie in Gondwana. Adding flavour to this was the existence of similar sedimentary strata in the Trans-Antarctic mountains that separate ancient East Antarctica from Phanerozoic West Antarctica. Just as interesting was the occurrence of a small patch of Grenvillian age in the Shackleton Hills of Antarctica, at the extremity of the great loop-like Grenvillian orogen (Figure 3.1), one of the main 'stitches' that held Gondwana together. They juxtaposed the two supposed sides of the 800 Ma sedimentary trough, after slicing off the later orogens of westernmost North America and West Antarctica. The SW America–East Antarctica connection, dubbed the SWEAT hypothesis by Moores, also brings in the known connections of

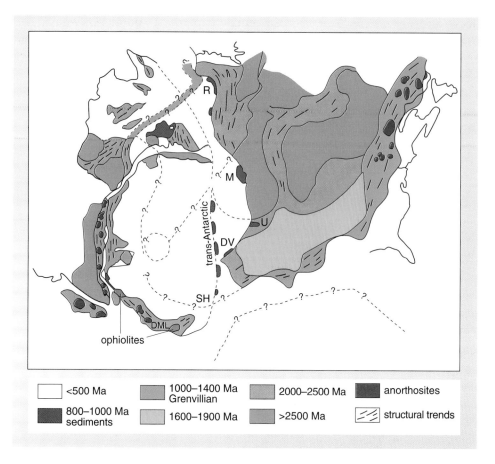

Figure 3.3 The SWEAT hypothesis linking North America to Gondwana along the line of the Trans-Antarctic Mountains (SH Shackleton Hills), as proposed by Moores and Dalziel in 1991. Note that Australia, Antarctica, India and Madagascar are shown in their Pangaea positions, when orogens of Grenvillian age were linked. Since 1991, the general connections between different Grenvillian orogens have become widely accepted, with some modifications as more data have been assembled.

Madagascar, India and western Australia with East Antarctica (Figure 3.3). The hypothetical SWEAT connection does one thing extremely well; it joins the great Grenvillian belt of North America to one with near-identical age and geology, which loops through the part of Gondwana that united Australia, Antarctica, India and Madagascar.

The Grenvillian orogen involved several continent–continent collisions. But the Grenvillian of North America has only one side against older continental crust (Figure 3.3). So where is its complement on the other side? It has to be some other old boundary marked by Grenvillian ages of deformation and metamorphism. In mid-1991, the SWEAT hypothesis was travelling through the geological community like wildfire, and another Precambrian specialist with a global perspective joined in the fun — Paul Hoffman, now of the University of Harvard. The present Pacific margin of South America is mainly buried beneath the Andes, which comprise an enormous mass of Mesozoic to Recent volcanic rocks erupted as a result of subduction of eastern Pacific plates. However, a sliver of Precambrian rocks along the Pacific coast of Peru near Arequipa, tiny by Andean standards, proved to have undergone Grenvillian deformation. That was enough for Hoffman and Dalziel to slide western South America against eastern North America and thereby grow a supercontinent that was older than 800 Ma in a thought-experiment. It was soon to be dubbed **Rodinia**, from the Russian for 'motherland', and the hypothesis left only Africa to be fitted into a great round continent surrounded by ocean — more of Africa shortly.

The concept of Rodinia, with North America sitting in the middle, posed the question of how later re-arrangements took place. For Hoffman, **Laurentia** (comprising North America together with other smaller fragments) and **Baltica**, which were welded along the original Grenvillian belt, had to have burst out to leave a vast oceanic gap between the remaining parts of Rodinia. Other authors have challenged that bold proposition. Whatever, various continental fragments may well have travelled half-way around the globe, and oceans must have been destroyed by subduction and island arc volcanism on a gigantic scale (Figure 3.4). Dramatic stuff.

Evidence that Rodinia did indeed exist up to about 750 Ma ago resulted from a flurry of attempts to confirm or refute the SWEAT hypothesis using paleomagnetic data. Sufficient paleopoles from all continental segments that existed in the 1100–750 Ma period are now available to show Rodinia fully assembled at around 750 Ma (Figure 3.4). It was a product of a unique global collision between all the segments that formed the 10 000-km-long Grenvillian orogen and trapped North America and East Antarctica in a log-jam of continental crust. The Trans-Antarctic Mountains, where 800 Ma sediments occur, are the most likely site for the beginning of Laurentia's escape. What happened to the rest of Rodinia is the subject of Sections 3.2.2 and 3.2.3, where the clock runs forward for half a billion years. In Section 3.2.4, we return to the earlier Precambrian.

In case you are wondering how the British Isles' evolution fits into this monumental hypothesis, Figure 3.4 shows the location of their northern component, trapped between Laurentia and Amazonia, near the 750 Ma equator. We do not show the southern parts, because they simply did not exist at that time.

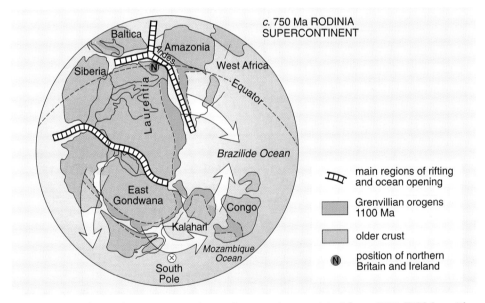

Figure 3.4   The Rodinia supercontinent that may have existed from 1100–750 Ma, with geological fits controlled by precise paleomagnetic pole data for its components. The map shows the positions of continental crust relative to the South Pole and Equator 750 Ma ago, including northern Britain and Ireland. Most of the present outlines of modern continents show up, but later crustal additions have been trimmed. Part of Brazil is shown attached to the Congo craton of Africa. The West Africa craton lies against Brazil and is almost hidden by the projection. North America (Laurentia) lies at the core of Rodinia. You will not find most of NE Africa and Arabia — they simply did not exist at that time. The Mozambique Ocean, shown at lower right, was the site for their formation. Large arrows show the general directions in which various fragments of Rodinia moved after its break-up.

3.2.2 Building Gondwana

This Section does not bear directly on the geological evolution of the British Isles, but outlines a series of huge events that followed the break-up of Rodinia, and assembled what was to become the southern part of Pangaea. You will not be assessed on its contents, though it forms part of the global context for Neoproterozoic events that contributed to uniting the different segments of continental lithosphere that make up the British Isles. Continental lithosphere that now underpins southern Britain formed at one flank of the Gondwana supercontinent. Spend a few moments comparing Figure 3.4 with the distribution of continental segments in Gondwana on Figure 3.1.

You should first look at Gondwana's Neoproterozoic orogens on Figure 3.1. These mark the sutures between older continental segments that assembled to make up this Paleozoic supercontinent. The fit of modern continents in Gondwana has been barely challenged since Wegener's day, and there is growing knowledge about the contents of the Neoproterozoic orogens that stitched its oldest components together. So, Figure 3.1 is an accepted model, and provides the clues to how Gondwana came into being after Rodinia broke apart.

The coherence of the Grenvillian orogen that runs through refitted Australia, Antarctica, India and Madagascar shows that part of Gondwana became united at around 1100 Ma — it is termed East Gondwana. On Figure 3.4, West Gondwana (Africa and South America on Figure 3.1) does not exist, its component parts being widely separated. Examining what happened to each major segment that contributed to West Gondwana gives an idea of how it came into being.

- Assume that the Rodinia model in Figure 3.4 is acceptable, and ignore the geographic framework of latitudes and longitudes. How did the segment made up of the Kalahari and Congo cratons of Africa move to reach its position in Gondwana?

- In Gondwana, the Kalahari–Congo segment abutted eastern South America and the West Africa segment. That implies a counter-clockwise movement of the first and a clockwise movement of South America and West Africa from their relative positions on Figure 3.4. The pivot (or pole of rotation) would have been somewhere inside the position of Laurentia on Figure 3.4.

- Can you suggest the motion of East Gondwana (India–Madagascar, Antarctica and Australia) to reach its position in Pangaea (Figure 3.1) from where it was in Rodinia?

- On Figure 3.1, East Gondwana abuts East Africa. To reach that position, it too must have rotated in a counter-clockwise sense to follow the motion of Kalahari–Congo and eventually collided with its eastern flank. Again, the likely pole of rotation would have been within Laurentia's position in Rodinia.

Now you should be able to grasp the significance of the huge 1000 to 500 Ma orogens that separate former parts of Rodinia, one running from West Africa into eastern South America, and the other dominating East Africa. Not only are they zones of continent–continent collision, but must contain remnants of whatever had formed in the oceans that separated the various segments of Gondwana on Figure 3.4.

- What process must have taken place in those oceans, in order that the various Gondwana segments could collide, and what would it have produced?

- The oceanic lithosphere between the three main segments of Gondwana must have been subducted, and that would have generated magmas to form island arcs and perhaps continental-margin volcanic belts, as you studied in Block 3.

Products of events between about 1000 and 500 Ma pervade West Gondwana. Collectively, those events are generally known as the **Pan-African orogeny** (Block 4, Figure 1.2), although they extend through much of Gondwana. The huge, wedge-like zone (the East African orogen) in NE Africa and western Arabia is made up almost entirely of oceanic-arc igneous rocks, and sediments derived from them, which show no evidence of having formed earlier than about 850 Ma (Figure 3.5). In this juvenile crust are lines along which ophiolites occur. These probably mark the former sites of subduction zones, above which island arcs formed. The smaller terranes between the ophiolitic belts each have their own petrological characteristics and histories. Some began to form as long ago as 850 Ma, and the youngest are about 650 Ma old. The last major orogenic events recorded in NE Africa and Arabia occurred about 550 Ma ago. Detailed studies of the deformation patterns inside the small terranes suggest that this assembly of accreted oceanic island arcs did not form simply by juvenile crustal

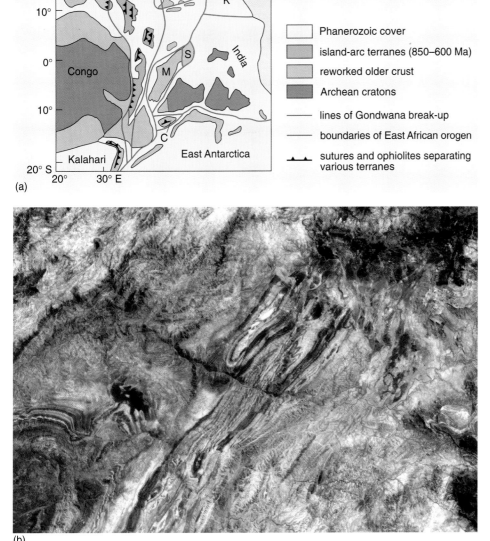

(a)

(b)

Figure 3.5   (a) The East African orogen, showing the extents of juvenile, Neoproterozoic crust, ophiolite belts that separate distinctly different terranes and older continental crust. Africa lies in its present geographic position. Abbreviations: C Ceylon (Sri Lanka); K Kerman Block (now part of eastern Iran); M Madagascar; S Seychelles Block (now in Indian Ocean). (b) Satellite image showing folded Neoproterozoic rocks in Northern Ethiopia, deformed during the Pan-African orogeny about 600 Ma ago.

slivers being squashed between two approaching segments of more ancient crust (East Gondwana and the cratons of Africa). Everywhere there are signs of immense strike–slip deformation, often with a sinistral sense of movement. Moreover, there are few zones of high-grade metamorphism that indicate large-scale crustal thickening in other orogens, such as the Himalaya. These lines of evidence suggest that somehow the East African orogen grew by many, once widely separated terranes being slid together laterally.

The East African orogen is not a parallel-sided orogenic belt. Instead, it narrows southwards to disappear in East Antarctica. Also, the proportion of juvenile crust in it decreases progressively southwards. In its southern part, instead of accreted island arcs the orogen consists of highly metamorphosed and deformed older crust — ancient continental material that was reworked during the collision of Kalahari–Congo and East Antarctica–India–Australia. Many geologists who have worked on the East African orogen consider that the patterns of juvenile material and deformation show that the jumble of island-arc terranes in NE Africa and Arabia probably were expelled from the zone where the cratons of southern Africa most closely approached the opposite side of the orogen. They escaped in the manner of peanut butter and banana from a toasted sandwich clutched by a hungry Elvis Presley (Block 4, Section 7.4.3).

The other great orogenic seam across which Gondwana came together is that which separated West Africa, and eastern South America from the western edge of Kalahari–Congo in Gondwana (Figure 3.1). In South America, this join is called the Brasilide Orogen. In West Africa, the suture is the Trans-Saharan orogen. They are one and the same, and their connection formed an important plank in Wegener's reconstruction of southern Pangaea. Deformation, metamorphism and igneous activity in West Africa and Eastern South America spans much the same period as in the East African Orogen. However, there are considerable differences, for the Brasilide Orogen contains abundant high-grade metamorphic rocks that provide evidence for crustal thickening around 650 to 600 Ma ago. It seems to have formed by head-to-head continental collision.

Hoffman's hypothesis that Laurentia, and other segments to the north of it on Figure 3.4, broke out from the core of Rodinia offers some assistance in grasping the formation of Gondwana. For Laurentia to emerge from the core of Rodinia demands the formation of oceanic lithosphere on a grand scale at the heart of the 1100-Ma-old supercontinent, starting along the line of fit between the Trans-Antarctic Mountains and SW North America. Sea-floor spreading in this ocean, together with all the slab-pull forces at subduction zones in the Brasilide and Mozambique Oceans needed to form abundant island arcs, could have driven the assembly of Gondwana. As yet, no-one has discovered evidence suggesting a cause for this immense event. Judging from the well-established link between the break-up of Pangaea and continental flood basalts that signify impact of mantle plumes at the base of the continental lithosphere (Block 2, Section 5), the break-up of the mother of all continents may have followed the daddy of all mantle plumes impacting its centre from below! But there are no commensurate continental flood basalts. However, geochemical studies of Pan-African ophiolites reveal close affinities of some to the submarine flood basalts dredged from the Ontong–Java Plateau of the western Pacific Ocean (Block 1). They possibly formed from such a plume.

3.2.3 What about the rest?

The British Isles' geological infrastructure stems largely from the assembly of what became the northern half of Pangaea. That was principally Laurentia, Siberia and Baltica (Figure 3.4). Curiously, for all the dominance of the southern supercontinent by orogenic events that peaked around 650 to 600 Ma, none of the large segments of northern Pangaea show much sign of this Pan-African frenzy of activity. Presumably, during the period from Rodinia break-up around 750 Ma through the Neoproterozoic, they drifted without encountering subduction at their margins. Charting their drift from that period to their amalgamation in Pangaea depends to a large extent on paleomagnetic pole data. Having been swarmed over by well-endowed Earth scientists, the continental segments of Laurentia, Baltica and western Europe provided much of those data.

Skipping through the time of dramatic events that assembled Gondwana to 580 Ma ago, paleomagnetic data reveal a framework for the main continental segments that eventually contributed to northern Pangaea. Figure 3.6 shows Laurentia, Baltica and Siberia in close association with what was to become South America. This is not at all like the 'fit' shown in Figure 3.1.

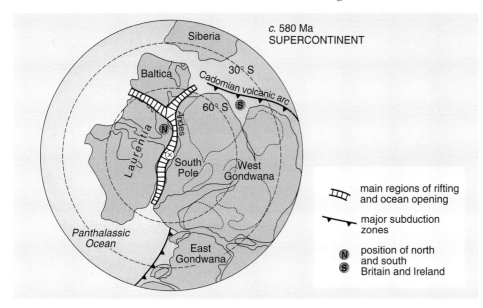

Figure 3.6 Paleogeographic map of continental segments 580 Ma ago. The break-up of Rodinia evolved towards re-assembly of another short-lived supercontinent, late in the Neoproterozoic. The positions of northern (N) and southern Britain and Ireland (S) are shown as red dots.

Locations that were destined to become part of the British Isles are shown as red dots on Figure 3.6. The striking thing about them is just how far apart they were. 'Proto-Scotland' lay close to the Laurentia–Baltica join. The fragment destined to become the Midland craton, at the core of England and Wales (Section 2), began to form in a system of island arcs — the Cadomian volcanic arc — above a subduction zone north of Amazonia–West Africa. Clearly, subsequent tectonics that eventually united these parts in the Pangaea supercontinent probably involved separations, rotations and considerable drifting. The likely zones of initial continental extension and break-up of the late-Neoproterozoic supercontinent appear on Figure 3.6.

Figure 3.7 shows 'snapshots' of global evolution through the critical period for the assembly of most of the British lithosphere. These are artistic impressions of the paleogeography of two hemispheres, plus a summary of plate tectonics that uses a Molleweide projection to cover the whole Earth. Note that both projections distort areas that lie at high latitudes. By 550 Ma ago (Figure 3.7a), Laurentia (with 'proto-Scotland'), Baltica and Siberia had parted company, with the formation of a RRR triple junction. These continental masses, which eventually became northern Pangaea, had separated from Gondwana, while volcanism continued at today's northern flank of that southern supercontinent, in the **Cadomian Arc**. A series of oceans had formed, which had to close over the next 250 Ma or so. Just before the start of the Cambrian Period, the world consisted of one supercontinent (Gondwana), the huge Panthalassic Ocean and three separate continental segments. Incidentally, break-up of the 580 Ma supercontinent resulted in increased length of coastlines and areas of shelf seas

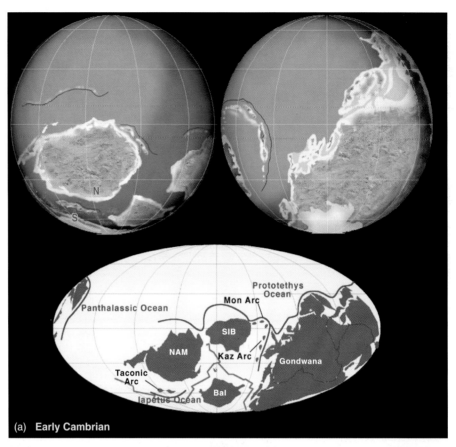

(a) **Early Cambrian**

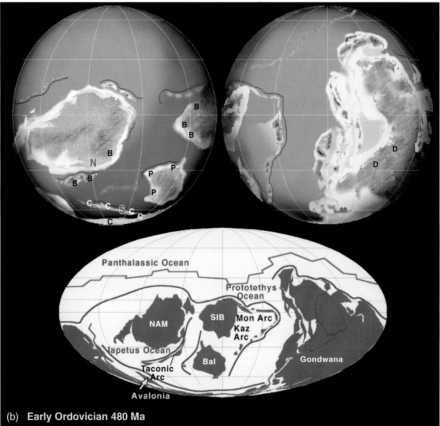

(b) **Early Ordovician 480 Ma**

Figure 3.7   Paleogeographic and tectonic maps showing the continental segments that were to become northern Pangaea. (a) Early Cambrian 540 Ma ago, with N and S Britain marked as N and S on the paleogeographic map. (b) Early Ordovician 480 Ma ago, showing different trilobite faunas (B, P, D and C) occupying distinct provinces.

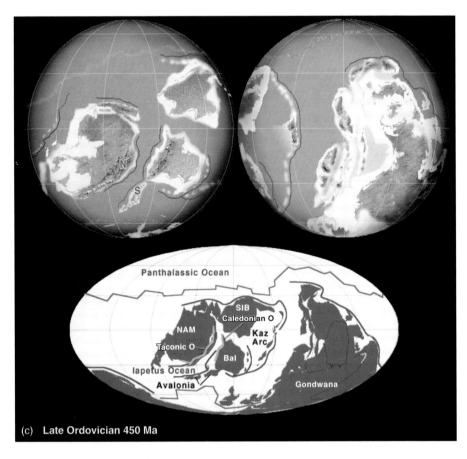

(c)   Late Ordovician 450 Ma

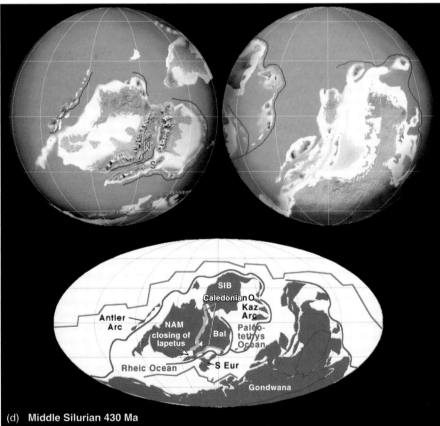

(d)   Middle Silurian 430 Ma

(c) The Late Ordovician at 450 Ma. (d) The Middle Silurian 430 Ma ago. On the tectonic maps, constructive margins are shown as red lines, destructive margins in blue and orogenic belts are shown by orange lines. Images kindly provided by Ronald Blakey, Northern Arizona University, USA. Full size versions are included on the Block 3 CD-ROM.

and therefore more ecological niches. Many paleontologists see these profound geographic changes as important factors in the explosive diversification of animals with skeletons at the beginning of the Phanerozoic Eon — the 'Cambrian Explosion' at about 544 Ma. The Iapetus Ocean that formed between Laurentia and Gondwana was central to the evolution of the British Isles and much of eastern North America. By 550 Ma, subduction on its northern part was forming a volcanic arc, known to North American geologists as the **Taconic Arc**, which, as you will learn, played an important role in the creation of Scotland.

Organic evolution and diversification provided another means of assessing the tectonic separation of continental segments during the early Phanerozoic. On Figure 3.7b, different letters indicate different assemblages of Early Ordovician trilobites that occur exclusively on some of the major segments. By the Early Ordovician, Gondwana had drifted across the South Pole, to place the small segments that were to become north and south Britain and Ireland on opposite sides of the Iapetus Ocean. Active spreading at its axis had ceased, to be replaced by spreading at the margin of Gondwana, so that the Cadomian Arc had by this time begun to rift from its parent continent.

● Can you suggest a mechanism for the start of active spreading that split the Cadomian Arc from Gondwana?

● Subduction had been beneath the Gondwana margin, where a back-arc basin may have developed, eventually to evolve into a fully fledged constructive margin.

You should remember from Block 4 (Section 3.1) that the Early to Middle Ordovician (between 470 to 460 Ma) saw the culmination of crustal deformation that involved the Dalradian sediments of the Scottish Highlands and northern Ireland. Block 4 suggested that deformation during the Grampian phase of the Caledonian orogeny was connected to collisional processes. However, paleomagnetic data for that time show no evidence for a major continent involved in collision with Laurentia and 'proto-Scotland'. The Early to Middle Ordovician event, in this series of reconstructions, involved accretion of the Taconic island arc to Laurentia (Figure 3.7b and c), in a similar fashion to that of Kohistan to Eurasia in the early stages of the formation of the Himalayan orogen (Block 4, Sections 7.2 and 7.3). The Grampian phase is the British term for the Taconic orogeny in North America. At least part of that mystery will be resolved in Section 5, when you will look in more detail at geological evidence from the British Caledonides. On Figure 3.7b and c, the initiation of the Grampian–Taconic orogeny is signified by subduction of the Iapetus Ocean beneath Laurentia. By the Late Ordovician (Figure 3.7c), the Cadomian volcanic arc, which had begun to form at the northern margin of Gondwana in the late Neoproterozoic (Figure 3.6), had become fully separated from it by the **Rheic Ocean**. This sliver of young continental material has been dubbed **Avalonia** (after the Avalon Peninsula in Newfoundland, rather than King Arthur's mythical realm). In it were what eventually became most of England, South Wales and southern Ireland, together with the present seaboard of the NE USA and eastern Canada (Figure 3.8).

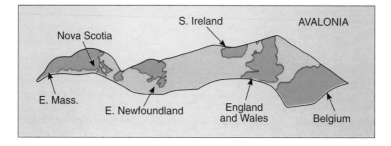

Figure 3.8   Schematic map showing England, Wales and Southern Ireland in relation to other continental fragments in Avalonia.

About 20 Ma later still, in the Middle Silurian, the Iapetus Ocean had almost been consumed by subduction (Figure 3.7d). The new Avalonian crust that had formed at its opposite side in the Cadomian Arc, was close to accretion with Laurentia. That process resembled the plastering of similar slivers to western North America during the Mesozoic, after they had travelled across the early eastern Pacific Ocean (Block 1, Section 1.4.3). Avalonia's shift through 40–50 degrees of latitude (a distance of 2400 to 3000 km) relative to Gondwana, but independently of Laurentia, required two factors: (i) subduction of Iapetus oceanic lithosphere at an average rate of around 50 mm per year, comparable with the rates in the West Pacific today (Block 1, Activity 1.1); and (ii) rifting of the northern flank of Gondwana to initiate fully fledged sea-floor spreading in the Rheic Ocean, which became comparable in size to Iapetus and in the same position relative to Laurentia and Gondwana.

Question 3.2 What significance do the positions of central Europe, most of France and the Iberian peninsula (the components of **Armorica** — the Celtic name for Brittany) (Figure 3.7c, d) have in relation to the Rheic Ocean? Roughly where must constructive and destructive plate boundaries have been at the time of Armorica's appearance?

The answer to Question 3.2 implies that the constructive margin driving both the Avalonia and Armorica microcontinents Laurentiawards must have shifted twice to the northern flank of Gondwana. Why that happened — and the paleomagnetic evidence strongly supports such shifts — is currently not much discussed.

Figure 3.7d shows the tectonic situation 30 Ma before the start of the movie sequence that you worked with in Activity 3.2, which covered the period since 400 Ma ago (Early Devonian). Armorica was destined to collide with 'proto-Britain' to produce the Variscan Front (Section 2). Figures 3.7c, d and 3.9 reveal important details of motions in the vicinity of 'proto-Britain'.

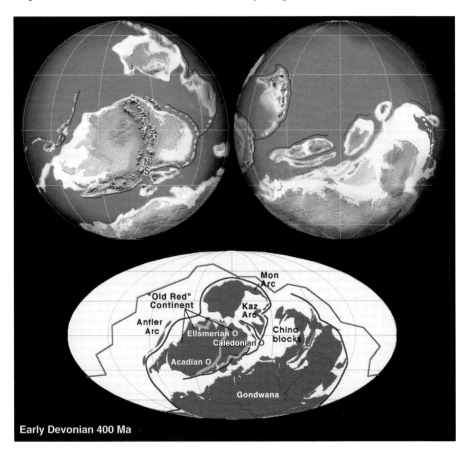

Early Devonian 400 Ma

Figure 3.9   Paleogeographic and tectonic maps for the Early Devonian (400 Ma), showing continental segments that were to become northern Pangaea. Images kindly provided by Ronald Blakey, Northern Arizona University, USA. Full-size versions are included on the Block 3 CD-ROM.

Question 3.3 Compare Figures 3.7d and 3.9. What motions other than those closing Iapetus can you see that affect the vicinity of 'proto-Britain'?

These readjustments, seemingly minor, form important factors in understanding the Lower Paleozoic evolution of the British Isles (Section 5). Figure 3.9 shows that, as far as the British Isles, Europe and Laurentia were concerned, the subsequent collision of Armorica was little different from that of Avalonia.

3.3 Early plate-tectonic events

Aside from the fact that geologists are considerably less certain about the architecture of Rodinia than about younger supercontinents, using orogenic belts older than the 1100-Ma-old Grenvillian, together with paleomagnetic pole data, should, in principle, enable them to chart even earlier relative motions of continental segments. Although a few geologists have speculated on such older assemblages and their break-up, the older rocks are the more likely it is that they have been thermally and mechanically affected by later orogenic events. There is a time-dependent 'blurring' of information. So, interpreting different kinds of evidence becomes more difficult further back in time. Thermal events can reset rocks' magnetization, as well as their radiometric ages, and deformation can alter the geometry of any preserved remanent magnetization, so that working out the former pole position is prone to large errors. Worse still, erosion of rocks from ancient upper crust simply strips away suitable material for the geophysicist to work with. Imprecision in dating suitable rocks further blurs the tectonic record.

In Section 3.2.3, you saw how dramatic changes in tectonics emerged in only a few tens of million years during the Paleozoic Era. For the period from 750 Ma ago, errors less than 10 Ma are nowadays easily achieved using suitable radiometric dating methods. Errors stem partly from the methods themselves and partly from the vagaries of the materials being dated. It is difficult to improve precision beyond about 1% of the age being sought. So for rocks more than a billion years old, errors become comparable with the times in which major tectonic events take place. There is yet another problem. Assembling data to erect believable and testable tectonic hypotheses takes time, effort and money. It required 10 years or more to collect those data from which the Neoproterozoic and early Paleozoic events in Section 3.2.3 were teased out; they cover about 250 Ma. Earlier times extend more than 3000 Ma further back, so that getting data of the necessary quality and quantity to do a similar job, even if it were possible, might take a very long time indeed.

In practice, Earth scientists are unable to chart movements of fragments of crust older than about one billion years, and can only speculate about the global tectonic evolution of earlier times. Assessing processes that constructed the most ancient parts of continents relies on data from isolated areas of different ages, usually 'windows of opportunity' that later events have left unscathed. Geologists have attempted to apply uniformitarian principles, seeing how far back they can apply them before they begin to break down. On a global scale, Hutton's famous principle assumes that present tectonic processes form the key to past evolution of the Earth system. Four general features signify modern tectonics:

1 sea-floor spreading from linear ridge systems (preserved in ophiolites);

2 mantle plumes (oceanic and continental flood basalt provinces);

3 steep subduction (high-P, low-T metamorphism, and calc-alkaline arc magmatism);

4 collisional orogeny (narrow, linear zones of deformed older crust).

The only sign of orogenic processes that contributed to the geology of the British Isles in the period between 1000 and 2700 Ma occurred around 1750 Ma, when older crustal segments joined and underwent reworking. It is virtually impossible to connect that event to others elsewhere, but we do examine this and earlier British events in Section 4.

The British Isles present a blank slate for more than a billion and a half years in the Precambrian. Information about that period from elsewhere is voluminous and growing rapidly. Because it bears little on British geology, and is yet to be connected in a context of global events, we spare you the details. What follows briefly covers the oldest proven occurrences of the four 'signatures' of tectonic processes that closely resemble modern ones.

1 *Ophiolites* similar to those obducted during the Mesozoic and Cenozoic Eras are unknown before a 2000-Ma-old example from Jormua in Finland, which occurs where an island arc accreted to an Archean continental mass 1900 Ma ago. Although highly deformed and metamorphosed, the Jormua ophiolite shows virtually every feature found in more modern examples. The sequence has a cap of turbidite sediments, formed as ocean floor approached a destructive margin to be flooded with debris derived from a volcanic arc.

2 *Continental flood basalts* form highly elevated plateaux, which are prone to erosion. So it is no surprise to find them missing from old continental segments. They emerged from linear fissures, so their former presence would be marked by swarms of basaltic dykes. These are common in Precambrian crustal segments, including one dated at 2400–2000 Ma in north-west Scotland (Section 4), the oldest known being the 3000 Ma Ameralik swarm in West Greenland. Many of them are hundreds of kilometres long, and dozens of dykes occur in each kilometre across the width of the swarms. These features suggest that huge volumes of magma may have reached the surface. Voluminous mafic lavas do occur in the early Precambrian, some reaching thicknesses up to 8 km. However, very few show signs of having been erupted subaerially onto stable continental crust (Section 4.5.2) — a characteristic of continental flood basalts of more modern times. Instead, thick early Precambrian mafic lavas generally show signs of having erupted in deep water, to help fill peculiar basinal structures known as **greenstone belts**, which are often floored by older felsic gneisses (Section 4.5.2).

3 *Steep subduction*, and by implication the existence of slab-pull force, has generated blueschists and eclogites throughout the Phanerozoic. Before these geologically recent times such high-*P*, low-*T* metamorphic rocks (Block 4, Sections 6.2.3 and 7.2.1) are almost as rare as hens with teeth. Eclogites as old as 3000 Ma occur as xenoliths in South African diamond-bearing kimberlites, but such inclusions came from far below ancient continental crust, with no sign of how they formed. High-*P*, low-*T* metamorphic assemblages are highly unstable when uplifted slowly by erosion, particularly so if they experienced later metamorphism under less extreme conditions. So their rarity is not unexpected. The oldest-known examples of high-*P*, low-*T* metamorphic rocks are from the 850–650-Ma-old Pan-African orogeny, and occur with ophiolites in north-western Eritrea. Steep subduction is also a prerequisite for the formation of narrow zones of magmatism in oceanic island arcs and volcanic continental margins, such as the Andes. The earliest concrete evidence for such volcanic arcs, dominated by andesitic magmas (Block 3), and their incorporation into continental crust by accretionary orogeny is no more than 2000 Ma old. In Archean complexes, andesites are rare (Section 4). However, other features that suggest linear magmatism in an arc-like setting occur in the wonderfully named Wabigoon Province of the Canadian Shield, and date from the latest part of the Archean (2700 Ma).

4   *Narrow, collisional orogens.* As long as blocks of felsic crust that cannot be subducted *en masse* existed, lateral motion of the lithosphere must inevitably have ensured that such fragments collided. In that sense, continent–continent collision would have been a normal occurrence since magmagenesis first involved processes that formed silica-rich magma. Its significance in demonstrating ancient examples of modern plate tectonics lies in how continental lithosphere deforms during collisions, when the bulk of it is strong and rigid. Block 4 discussed the best example of a collisional orogen in the Himalaya, which is narrow compared with its length and characterized by brittle processes, at least in the upper crust. The earliest accepted evidence for collisional orogens of Himalayan type occurs in the 2000-Ma-old Paleoproterozoic of Canada and Australia.

'Firsts' for any complete signs of modern plate-tectonic processes extend no further back than the late Archean, and most are Proterozoic in age. Is there something special about the Archean Eon, or is it just so gnarled by later processes that it is simply an incorrigible mess? Meeting the Archean challenge relies on blending theoretical considerations with evidence from parts of the continental lithosphere that formed before 2500 Ma ago. In the second respect, British Earth scientists have been endowed with a 'piece of the action': exposures of the Lewisian Complex in the Hebridean Terrane (inset to Tectonic Map). In Section 4, you will begin by examining the British Isles' oldest rocks.

3.4   Summary of Section 3

- During the break-up of the Pangaea supercontinent, the British Isles' position near to its centre involved it in several episodes of extensional tectonics during the Mesozoic Era — it was far from destructive margins. In the early Cenozoic, the North Atlantic began to form, and the Hebrides and County Antrim show evidence for igneous activity during early attempts at sea-floor spreading.

- Discoveries about ancient plate tectonics progressed backwards in time, as paleomagnetic techniques improved and were applied to rocks of increasing age and complexity on all major continents. Also, increasing knowledge of pre-Pangaea orogenic belts, particularly their age of formation and how they evolved, allowed likely 'ties' between formerly united masses to be evaluated. Some fit well on Pangaea, but others of different age ranges and in different parts of Pangaea do not. Since orogens and evidence for arc magmatism relate to linear, destructive margins, of which there are a limited number today, it is theoretically possible, by 'shuffling' the continental blocks where they occur, to connect them in rational patterns that would reflect not only older plate tectonics, but former supercontinents. This is only plausible when combined with paleomagnetic data.

- Gondwana, the southern part of Pangaea, existed as a supercontinent throughout the first half of the Phanerozoic Eon. Laurasia, the northern part, assembled over that period from several crustal segments that were widely separated at the outset of the Phanerozoic. Gondwana's assembly dates to the Neoproterozoic (between 650 and 550 Ma). That event welded components of Africa and South America, that comprised West Gondwana. However, what became East Gondwana (Australia, Antarctica, India and Madagascar) contained a linked system of orogens that formed about 1100 Ma ago. It was an older supercontinent. Mountain-building events around 1100 Ma also occurred in North America and Scandinavia (Laurentia and Baltica), and in a few places in Africa and South America, so it seems that period was one of enormous tectonic activity on a global scale. Attempts to connect these Grenvillian orogens together first united East Gondwana with western Laurentia, on geological grounds. As geophysicists collected more paleomagnetic pole data, it became clear that all continental crust formed part of a Pangaea-sized supercontinent from 1100 to about 750 Ma, although there is not complete agreement on the details of the refit. That mass was dubbed Rodinia, from the Russian word for Motherland.

- The great importance of Rodinia's recognition is two-fold. First, it represents the starting point for the 450 million years of continental drift, plate tectonics and all that they entail as regards Earth processes, which culminated in the last unification of all continental material in Pangaea about 300 Ma ago. Secondly, once a well-supported refit of all pre-1100 Ma continental crust emerges, it may become possible to treat all the evidence for older plate tectonics in much the same way as the sutures, orogenic belts and products of magmatic arcs of younger times have helped chart later global history. There is a third aspect to Rodinia. Its break-up, and partial reassembly in Gondwana, spanned a period when events of enormous importance affected the climate and the biosphere. Between 750 and 550 Ma, the climate seems to have been thrown repeatedly into near-catastrophic periods of cooling that may have coated the entire planet in ice — the 'Snowball Earth' events of which you may have heard. Also, it was in the tectonic and climatic contexts of that time that multicelled life forms, and eventually animals with skeletons emerged — the critical stage in our own origins.

- Tracking the post-Rodinia positions of the three fundamental continental blocks (Laurentia, Gondwana and Baltica) is the tectonic key to the Neoproterozoic and Paleozoic evolution of the British lithosphere. The British Isles' component parts formed far apart on the globe. Scotland and the north of Ireland were part of pre-750 Ma Laurentia, whereas most of England, Wales and Southern Ireland only began to form after Rodinia broke up, on the flank of Gondwana (roughly where North Africa and northern South America abutted in Pangaea). Eventually, by Cambrian times, drift of Laurentia and Gondwana placed these precursors of the British Isles on opposite sides of the large, spreading Iapetus Ocean, the north on an initially passive margin, the south above a series of subduction zones at a destructive margin. Subduction, periodically at both sides, gradually closed the Iapetus Ocean. However tectonics can involve 'flips' from compression at destructive margins to extension and the formation of new ocean basins in the same geographic location. Two episodes of extension at the margin of Gondwana shed small continental masses (Avalonia and Armorica), that sea-floor spreading drove towards the opposite side of a complex of evolving oceans that separated the two giant continents. Eventually, their addition to Laurentia assembled the entire British lithosphere at the end of the Paleozoic Era. That evolution forms the framework for grasping the full significance of British geological evidence from 750 to 300 Ma.

- Recent attempts to rationalize geological features that formed during Precambrian times before the assembly of Rodinia have met with mixed success. The four main geological elements that Earth scientists have associated since the 1960s with the modern dynamics of the mantle and lithosphere are: ophiolites (evidence of sea-floor spreading); flood basalts (formed by mantle plumes); steep subduction; and narrow zones of collisional orogeny. All four show up in the geological record as far back as the start of the Proterozoic Eon. However, despite excellent exposures in the older Archean rocks, the trail for most of these features runs cold in the older Archean Eon.

Objectives for Section 3

Now that you have completed this Section, you should be able to:

3.1 Understand the meaning of all the terms printed in **bold**.

3.2 Recognize the paleomagnetic and geological evidence used in continental reconstructions before about 200 Ma.

3.3 Use paleogeographic maps and plate-tectonic reconstructions to suggest geological processes that were going on in a variety of global settings.

3.4 Visualize the global tectonic processes that contributed to the assembly of the British lithosphere in the period from 750 to 400 Ma.

3.5 Appreciate the probability that plate tectonics did not operate in its modern form during the earlier part of the Archean Eon.

Question 3.4 Describe the changes in paleolatitude involved in the motions of northern and southern Britain from 750 to 400 Ma.

4 The Lewisian, Archean processes and how cratons form

The Archean Eon occupied almost half of Earth's history, but the Lewisian, its representative in NW Scotland, represents only a fraction of that time. Because the principal traces of modern tectonic processes only show up convincingly in post-Archean rocks, Earth scientists have long disputed whether or not such processes explain geological features in Archean exposures. In this Section, you will be able to revise some of the more difficult concepts from Blocks 1, 2 and 3 in assessing the evidence for processes that vanished at the close of the Archean. Part of that study is assisted by features of the Lewisian, but it requires a brief examination of much larger assemblages of Archean rocks on other continents.

Every modern continent exposes Archean rocks, older than 2500 Ma. These relics suggest that continental 'nuclei' formed during that time. Figure 4.1 shows the distribution of areas that remained structurally unchanged by tectonic events since 1000 Ma ago. Each shaded area is a **craton**, and those which stabilized before 2500 Ma are not the only repositories of Archean rocks. Many cratons that became stable in the Proterozoic Eon contain abundant pre-2500 Ma rocks that later tectonic and thermal processes 'overprinted'. Later in this Section, we briefly draw out some typical features of Archean geology found in globally important areas. But first, we focus on our own patch of Archean crust.

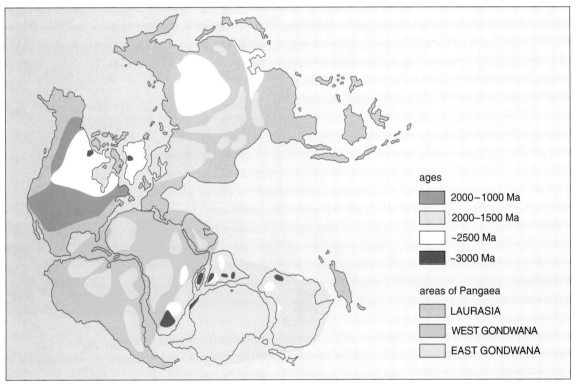

ages
- 2000–1000 Ma
- 2000–1500 Ma
- ~2500 Ma
- ~3000 Ma

areas of Pangaea
- LAURASIA
- WEST GONDWANA
- EAST GONDWANA

Figure 4.1 Distribution of cratonic areas, where tectonic activity ceased before 1000 Ma ago, in modern continents assembled in the Pangaea supercontinent.

Does the Lewisian Complex offer any tests of hypotheses about how the Earth worked in its early days or any explanations of the features seen in larger Archean complexes? It is by no means an ideal source of information, being a product of repeated deformation and metamorphism of rocks that formed the original Lewisian crust. That reworking involved three orogenic events over a period of about 1400 Ma. Only after resolving which Lewisian materials are the least modified since they emerged from the mantle is it possible to look for signs of how the Lewisian crust originated.

Activity 4.1

Now do Activity 4.1, centred on the video *The Lewisian of NW Scotland*, which introduces you to a classic area of British geology. Field observations in this part of the Lewisian Complex provided the main keys to unravelling the evolution of deep continental crust. Viewing the video and reading the associated notes should take you about an hour.

4.1   Establishing a chronology for Lewisian evolution

Ideas in *The Lewisian of NW Scotland*, and indeed all research into this ancient basement, stem from a very simple observation in Sutherland, made at the end of the 19th century by two indefatigable field mappers, Benjamin Peach and John Horne. The duo produced the first detailed geological maps and descriptions of NW Scotland that created a framework for all later work on the outer zone of the Caledonian orogen, the Moine Thrust Belt (Block 4, Section 3.1), as well as its foreland. They discovered a swarm of mafic to ultramafic dykes that cut the compositional banding in the gneisses that dominate the Lewisian. Yet the dykes are foliated and folded, which clearly indicate ductile strain during tectonic events that occurred after their intrusion. New minerals grew in such deformed dykes, so that event also involved changed thermal conditions. Every dyke shows some evidence for this metamorphism, but in some areas it affects only a few centimetres at their margins, whereas elsewhere dykes and the older gneisses that they intrude are thoroughly reconstituted. At least two orogenies contributed to the Lewisian's complexity, but the effects of the last are confined to more or less distinct zones. Beyond these zones of crustal reworking lie the undisturbed products of the earlier, pre-dyke event.

Everywhere, the dyke swarm and two sets of deformed Lewisian rocks that they distinguish sit beneath the most profound unconformity in Europe (Figure 2.1a), which takes the form of a rugged landscape that later sediments buried. Those sediments, mainly terrestrial sandstones, are known collectively as the Torridonian (Section 5.1.1). Since shallow-marine Cambrian sediments rest unconformably upon the Torridonian, the latter are by definition Precambrian, and are roughly 1000 Ma old. By the turn of the 19th century, it became clear that complexity in the Lewisian was the outcome of the oldest geological processes known in the British Isles.

Until the 1950s, geologists largely ignored the Lewisian, probably because Peach and Horne seemed to have 'said it all'. There is a grain of truth in that, because later attempts to radiometrically date the sequence of events have not changed the basic story very much. During their honeymoon at Scourie in Sutherland, the late John Sutton and Janet Watson of Imperial College, London revisited one of Peach and Horne's Lewisian stamping grounds. It spans the boundary between an area dominated by pre-dyke events and one overwhelmed by those which followed their intrusion. Rediscovering the Victorian duo's evidence, Sutton and Watson gave local names to the two episodes: Scourian for the first, after the village of Scourie (it is now known as the Badcallian after a nearby hamlet); and Laxfordian for the second, because its effects appear suddenly when one approaches Loch Laxford from the south (Figure 4.2). Later work around Lochinver by others in the 1960s showed that structures in the oldest part of the complex underwent ductile deformation and metamorphic reworking in shear zones, before the intrusion of the dykes. A third tectonic event entered Lewisian lore: the Inverian.

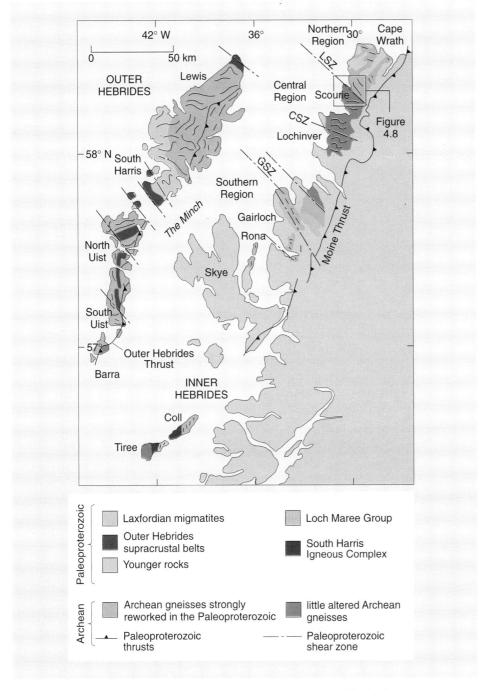

Figure 4.2   Division of the Lewisian of NW Scotland: various blocks, boundaries, dominant ages of protoliths and reworking, and rough trends of fabrics. LSZ Laxford Shear Zone; CSZ Canisp Shear Zone; GSZ Gairloch Shear Zone. Close-up of Laxford Front (same as LSZ) outlined (Figure 4.8).

The Tectonic Map shows just how small the Archean occurrences are in relation to those that formed later in the evolution of the British Isles. Compared with the size of Archean cratons on a world scale (Figure 4.1), the Lewisian's spatial significance is not overwhelming. Yet there is nowhere on the planet where measurements of the dip of fabrics and plunges of lineations, numbers of interfering fold generations, hand specimens, thin sections, geochemical analyses and isotopic determinations reach such a density per square kilometre. Some areas have been mapped at scales up to 1 : 1000 (the usual scale for civil engineering plans). It may therefore come as a surprise to learn that the Lewisian story is not yet 'done and dusted'; a good indicator of what remains to be learned from the rest of the Archean. Rarely a year passes without some heated dispute on the finer points of the Lewisian. Here is a summary of the most recent work on significant events recorded by the Lewisian.

Formation of Lewisian crust by mantle melting processes occurred before 2800 Ma. Felsic gneisses from the Northern Region of the Lewisian (extensively reworked by the Laxfordian events) contain igneous zircon grains giving that age. Zircons from the Central Region immediately to the south are significantly older, around 3000 Ma, suggesting that where *The Lewisian of NW Scotland* was filmed the Lewisian is a composite of two geologically distinct blocks separated by the boundary between pre- and post-dyke crustal reworking (LSZ, Figure 4.2). Although disputed since publication and yet to be replicated, Pb–Pb and Sm–Nd ages of 3300 Ma have been reported for mafic gneisses in the Central Region, which are similar to parts of the mafic–ultramafic masses shown in the video. However, dating by the Re–Os method gives ages of 2700 Ma. Whether the mafic–ultramafic complexes pre-date the gneisses or formed close in time to their incorporation into the Lewisian Complex has not been resolved. The mafic–ultramafic masses show geochemical affinities to oceanic lithosphere, and may be analogous to those in the much older Isua supracrustals of West Greenland (Section 4.5.1). Radiometric dating of pre-dyke gneisses that later events barely affected consistently shows initial metamorphism of continental crust at 2700 Ma — the Badcallian. A locally recognized event — the Inverian — modified Badcallian structures about 2500 Ma ago, before dyke intrusion occurred. The dykes themselves turn out not to represent a single pulse of basaltic magma, but span a period from 2400 to 2000 Ma. There are Paleoproterozoic supracrustal rocks in the Lewisian Complex near to Gairloch, and also in the Hebrides, where they are associated with a suite of calc-alkaline intrusions (Figure 4.2). Both have provided ages of about 1900 Ma. The Laxfordian reworking, whose discovery was a triumph of field geology, is not Archean at all. Its isotopic imprint dates from 1750 Ma ago.

The most important Lewisian rocks are those which have remained chemically and isotopically unchanged since high-grade Badcallian metamorphism. Although they are a billion years younger than the oldest crust in Greenland and Canada (Section 4.5), they *are* Archean. If there were processes going on during the Archean Eon that were significantly different from those that dominated post-Archean times, then Badcallian rocks should reveal geochemical signs of them.

4.1.1 Summary of Section 4.1

- The relative division of events that contributed to the evolution of the Lewisian centres on their relationships to a widespread dyke swarm, known as the Scourie dykes. These intrusions cut structures formed in an early orogeny (Badcallian), and are deformed by a later one (Laxfordian). The Lewisian Complex is overlain unconformably by the unmetamorphosed, terrestrial Torridonian sandstones. They lie beneath Cambro-Ordovician sediments.

- The earliest events in any segment of continental crust are those that generated magmas from which the crust originally formed — partial melting at mantle depths. Radiometric dating of zircons within the Lewisian gneisses divides the complex into two regions, which probably formed separately — the Northern Region, formed around 2800 Ma, and the Central Region that gives zircon U–Pb dates around 3000 Ma. Mafic–ultramafic masses may be older, but have not yielded unambiguous dates.

- The earliest orogenic event in the Lewisian was high-grade metamorphism and intense deformation at 2700 Ma in the Central Region, followed by a localized event about 2500 Ma ago. The Scourie dykes range in age from 2400 to 2000 Ma, rather than having been emplaced in a single episode, as was originally thought. Laxfordian deformation and metamorphism was at 1750 Ma. As well as affecting the Archean gneiss complex, Laxfordian deformation and metamorphism are also evident in Paleoproterozoic supracrustal and intrusive igneous rocks in the Hebrides and near Gairloch.

4.2 Archean geochemistry and tectonics

In Blocks 2 and 3, you learned how geochemical features can help model the processes that contribute to the formation of magmas in various tectonic settings.

● What are the three fundamental processes of this kind?

● They are partial melting in the mantle, fractional crystallization at the base of the crust, and assimilation of pre-existing crustal rocks.

4.2.1 Felsic igneous rocks

Figure 4.3 shows abundances of key trace elements, normalized to the estimated composition of the Earth's original mantle, in a felsic Lewisian gneiss from the Central Region and a felsic intrusion from the Andes. Both are markedly depleted in niobium (Nb). That feature is characteristic of igneous rocks in modern subduction-zone settings (Block 3, Section 3.2.2, Figure 3.2), although its origin is uncertain. There are several notable differences between the two materials. Ignore the much lower Rb, U and Th in the Lewisian rock — they were probably expelled to higher crustal levels during the Badcallian event (Activity 4.1).

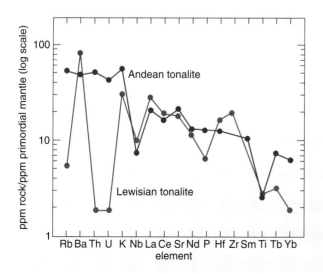

Figure 4.3   Plots of trace elements normalized to primitive mantle for an anhydrous, granulite-facies Lewisian gneiss of felsic composition from the Central Region (red) and a Tertiary igneous intrusion from the Andes (dark purple) that has roughly the same bulk composition.

Question 4.1 (a) How do the normalized abundances of light (La, Ce and Nd) REE and heavy REE (Sm, Tb and Yb) in the Lewisian sample differ from those in that from the Andes? (b) If you do notice a difference, what mineral(s) would have been involved in the evolution of the Lewisian sample?

Your answer to Question 4.1 suggests that the greater depletion of HREE relative to LREE in felsic Lewisian gneisses compared with Andean felsic intrusions implies that garnet remained as a solid phase when the gneisses' parent magma formed. Garnet is not implicated in modern subduction-zone magmagenesis. The evolution of felsic magmas that contribute to modern volcanic arcs involves fractional crystallization of more mafic magma at the base of the crust, i.e. under low-pressure conditions (Block 3, Section 4). That process involves residual plagioclase feldspar, olivine and pyroxene, in order to generate an evolved felsic magma. Garnet is unlikely to have crystallized from mafic magma at the temperature and pressure at the base of the crust.

Figure 4.4 shows REE plots for unmetamorphosed felsic intrusions (tonalites) and a tholeiitic basalt from the Archean of Minnesota, USA. The Minnesota tonalites are similar to the Lewisian gneiss. Rare-earth elements in the Archean tholeiite are little different from those found in modern island-arc tholeiites (Block 3, Figure 4.13). The Archean felsic pattern cannot have been derived from the mafic one by fractional crystallization at the base of the crust.

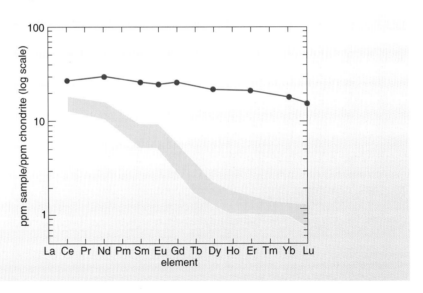

Figure 4.4   REE plots of unmetamorphosed felsic intrusions (pink field encompassing variations), and a mafic lava (red), from the Archean of Minnesota, USA.

The broad pattern of REE in a Lewisian felsic gneiss and its difference from that in a much younger felsic pluton is not a local peculiarity, as you can see from Figure 4.5a. There the difference between LREE and HREE is expressed by the ratio between normalized La and Yb abundances (La_N/Yb_N) plotted against Yb_N for many Archean and post-Archean felsic intrusions. The Archean and post-Archean data fall in two very different fields, the first with rapidly increasing La_N/Yb_N ratio as Yb_N falls, and the post-Archean rocks showing a wide variation in Yb and little variation in the ratio. Whatever the magmatic processes involved in the evolution of the two large sets of data, they were fundamentally different.

The model accepted for evolution of felsic magmas by fractional crystallization beneath modern volcanic arcs (Block 3, Section 4) fits the post-Archean data very well (Figure 4.5b). Solid lines on Figure 4.5b indicate various amounts of partial melting of mantle peridotite (estimated mean composition P) that produce

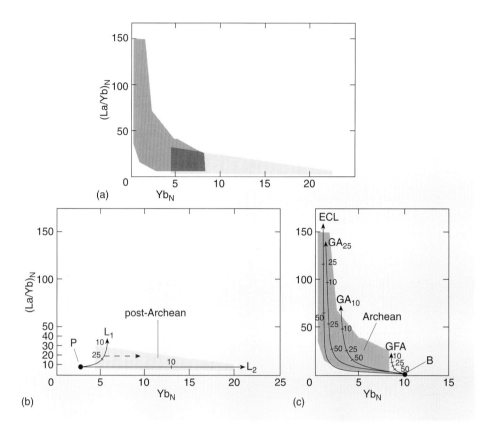

Figure 4.5 Plots of La_N/Yb_N against Yb_N for (a) Archean (red) and post-Archean (pink) plutonic rocks of broadly felsic composition. (b) Post-Archean data compared with modelled lines of liquid evolution (L_1 and L_2) from two basaltic parental magmas. Those magmas formed by varying degrees of melting of peridotite (composition P) with two different mineralogies (see below), and fractional crystallization of olivine (dashed line with arrowhead). (c) Archean data compared with lines linking compositions of magmas formed by different degrees of partial melting of mafic source material with the average composition of all analysed Archean basalts (B). Each source rock had different mineralogies (ECL, GFA and GA), explained below. In (b) and (c), the numbers against the various lines indicate the percentage of melting.

basaltic magma. The line $P–L_1$ is for garnet-bearing peridotite (involved in the generation of some plume-related basalts, as you saw in Block 2, Section 2.6.3), and $P–L_2$ shows basalts formed by partial melting of garnet-free peridotite (implicated in generation of modern ocean-ridge and subduction-zone basalts).

⬤ What are the main influences over enrichment in Yb in Figure 4.5b? You may need to refer to Block 2, Table 2.7 and Block 3, Figure 4.17.

⬤ Ytterbium has low K_d values between melt and olivine and pyroxene, being highly incompatible in those minerals. For $P–L_1$, garnet in the residue of melting retains Yb, so that the element has a low concentration in the melt. Only olivine fractionation can increase Yb in a melt formed originally from garnet peridotite. In $P–L_2$ only olivine and pyroxene remain in the residue of mantle melting, and their low K_d values add Yb to melts derived from garnet-free peridotite. In this case, the smaller the percentage of melting, the more Yb enters the melt.

So, as regards their REE patterns, the post-Archean felsic intrusions clearly fit the model given in Block 3, Section 4, and retain the low La_N/Yb_N signature of their parental mafic magmas because olivine (and pyroxene) fractionation leaves the ratio unchanged.

Now look at the Archean data in Figure 4.5c.

⬤ Could partial melting of garnet–peridotite create the range of La_N/Yb_N values in a basaltic magma that might have been parental to the Archean data? Would fractionation of olivine from such a basalt magma result in the spread of Archean Yb_N?

○ No, on both counts. Garnet would have to be extracted from the basalt during fractional crystallization at the base of the crust to amplify La_N/Yb_N ratios so much, which is highly unlikely. To increase silica and reduce MgO while generating a felsic magma by fractional crystallization needs the removal of olivine. That would drive Yb_N in the remaining felsic magma to *higher* values than that of point B, the average composition of all Archean basalts, whereas Yb_N in Archean felsic rocks is *lower* than in basalts of the same age.

A model involving fractional crystallization from a mafic parent magma cannot explain the LREE enrichment and HREE depletion of Archean felsic rocks. At least for these elements, it seems inescapable that the bulk of Archean continental crust did not form in the same way as occurs today beneath destructive margins and which seems to have characterized all felsic magmas younger than 2500 Ma. There remains only one option, i.e. that somehow the spread of Archean data stems from partial melting of a mafic source. Experimental melting shows that felsic liquids can form in such a way, provided the source is wet. The four solid lines on Figure 4.5c show some options. Line GFA is for melting of a garnet-free amphibolite, the two GA lines result from partial melting of amphibolite with 10 and 25% garnet, and ECL is for partial melting of eclogite (garnet–pyroxene rock of mafic composition). In each case, the different starting mineralogies have the composition of average Archean basalt — B. Although the real process was probably more complex and may have varied from place to place, models based on a metamorphosed basalt that contains garnet *can* recreate the actual spread of Archean felsic plutons.

Rather than partial melting of the mantle wedge above subduction zones, from which material was added to the post-Archean continents, partial melting of basaltic crust generated Archean continental crust. Assuming that continental material has always been added at destructive margins, your deductions suggest a fundamental change from **slab melting** before 2500 Ma ago, to **wedge melting** thereafter.

Figure 4.6 compares REE plots for a typical Lewisian felsic gneiss with one for a Tertiary plutonic rock with a similar, tonalitic composition.

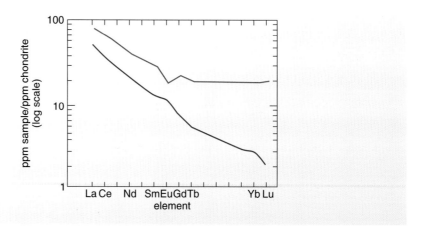

Figure 4.6 REE pattern for Lewisian felsic gneiss (purple) and Andean tonalite (red).

○ Apart from the different LREE and HREE, what else strikes you about the two plots in Figure 4.6?

○ The Lewisian gneiss (and also the unmetamorphosed Archean felsic intrusions in Figure 4.5) shows no significant europium (Eu) anomaly, whereas the post-Archean data show a prominent negative Eu anomaly.

The only common minerals with high K_d values for Eu are the feldspars (Block 3, Section 4.2.6, Figure 4.17). A negative Eu anomaly in an igneous rock indicates the separation of feldspar crystals from the parent magma during its evolution, almost certainly during fractional crystallization at the base of the crust. The post-Archean tonalite reflects such a process nicely. The magma from which the Lewisian tonalite formed did not have feldspar extracted from it.

So, the REE data from Archean felsic rocks strongly suggest two things: before 2500 Ma, continental crust formed from magmas generated by partial melting of garnetiferous mafic rocks; it shows little sign of having evolved from a mafic parent magma by fractional crystallization.

The Lewisian sample, for which geochemical data are given in Figure 4.3, contains metamorphic minerals that suggest it resided at least 35 km below the surface during the Badcallian event. It represents deep Archean crust. Unfortunately, erosion has removed the Lewisian upper crust completely — the gneisses of the Northern Region (Figure 4.2) represent middle crustal levels. The next Section shows how it is possible to estimate upper-crustal composition to see if there are processes involved in generation of continental crust that result in geochemical fractionation between its upper and lower parts. The processes thought to dominate crust formation in modern volcanic arcs (Block 3, Section 4) imply that post-Archean continents consist of two compositions: a lower crust dominated by cumulates formed by fractional crystallization; and an upper crust derived by crystallization of highly evolved felsic magmas. As you will see later, if the Archean crust was not fractionated in that way, there may have been profound differences between the strengths of Archean and more modern continents.

4.2.2 Composition of the Archean upper crust

Sediments, particularly fine-grained ones, are bulk samples of the upper crust exposed to erosion at the time of their deposition. There are none in the British Isles that formed at the same time as the Lewisian, but there are plenty of Archean shales elsewhere. Figure 4.7 shows REE patterns for some of them and for superficially identical rocks from the post-Archean record.

- How do the two sets differ?

- All the post-Archean samples show a small negative Eu anomaly, whereas the Archean shales do not.

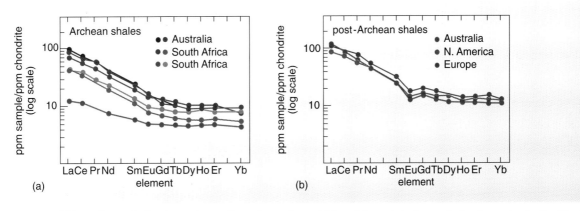

Figure 4.7   REE plots of (a) Archean shales from Australia and southern Africa; (b) post-Archean shales from Australia, North America and Europe.

Small as it is, the negative Eu anomaly in post-Archean shales reflects fractional crystallization of feldspar from the parents of magmas that contributed to the upper crust. Felsic igneous rocks in modern volcanic arcs also show negative Eu anomalies, for the same reason. The lack of such an anomaly in all Archean shales suggests that feldspar played no such role before 2500 Ma; there was no significant fractionation of magmas at the base of the crust, nor much within the crust itself. The first conclusion is borne out by samples of post-Archean deep crust brought to the surface tectonically or as inclusions in later volcanic rocks. They are dominated by mafic rocks, many showing evidence of having formed as cumulates, and they commonly contain positive Eu anomalies. Archean deep-crustal materials, represented by the anhydrous Badcallian gneisses, are dominantly felsic rocks that show no Eu anomalies.

4.2.3   Strength of the Archean continental lithosphere

Estimates of the strength of modern continental lithosphere are based on a two-layer model of the crust: upper crust dominated by quartz-rich rocks; and a more mafic lower crust of feldspar and ferromagnesian silicates (Block 1, Section 3). The evidence from Section 4.2.2 suggests that Archean continental crust was felsic from top to bottom.

- What does that imply for the strength of the Archean continental lithosphere compared with its younger equivalent under the same geothermal conditions?

- Archean continental lithosphere would have been weaker, as the feldspar + ferromagnesian silicate lower crust of more recent times imparts most of the strength to younger crust.

There is a paradox as regards Archean crust. On the one hand it imparts potential weakness to the whole lithosphere beneath it, from which you might expect that it would be prone to reworking in later orogenies. On the other, Archean crust forms the stable core of many modern continents (Figure 4.1), much of which has remained almost unchanged for more than 2500 Ma. There are other cratons made of rocks that separated from the mantle in more recent times, such as that underlying much of NE Africa and Arabia (formed between 850 and 650 Ma). Resolving the paradox needs a little thought.

- Given the inherent potential weakness of crust that is quartz-rich from top to bottom, what might ensure that it remains rigid, relative to newer additions to the continents?

- Continental rigidity becomes increasingly likely with lower surface heat flow, whatever its structure.

Figures 2.10 and 3.13 in Block 1 show how surface heat flow on the continents falls off with crustal age since the last significant orogenic event, from around 70–80 mW m^{-2} for the last 500 Ma to half that for areas older than about 1000 Ma. For surface heat flow less than 50 mW m^{-2}, no part of the continental lithosphere, whether having a two- or single layer crust, satisfies the conditions for ductile deformation (Block 1, Figure 3.11).

- What must underlie such geothermally cool areas?

- Rock whose overall content of heat-producing isotopes is low relative to that beneath areas of higher heat flow.

For the Lewisian, Figure 4.3 shows that the deep-crustal gneisses of the Central Region are extremely depleted in U, Th, and to a lesser extent K, relative to modern upper crustal igneous rocks. Once that geochemical difference became established, heat flow through the crust of the Central Region would have had virtually no contribution from its deepest part, except for that from the mantle, around 40 mW m^{-2}. The anhydrous Badcallian gneisses are products of deep-crustal metamorphism that took place at about 2700 Ma, when the continental lithosphere behaved in a pervasively ductile manner (Activity 4.1). Thereafter, only localized deformation took place in the Central Region, the final phase being the Laxfordian event almost a billion years later. The orogeny at 2700 Ma created a craton from what originated as extremely weak crust with high heat flow. The proof that heat-producing isotopes were driven from the deep crust during the Badcallian event is the Central Region's rigidity after high-grade metamorphism.

4.2.4   Summary of Section 4.2

- The calc-alkaline affinities of Lewisian gneisses, and all Archean felsic igneous rocks, together with their depletion in niobium, suggest that they formed from magmas generated at subduction zones. However, compared with superficially similar rocks from post-Archean magmatic arcs, Archean felsic rocks are strongly depleted in heavy rare-earth elements, which signifies the presence of garnet in the residue of partial melting. Garnet is not implicated in modern arc magmatism. Unlike post-Archean crust, which formed by partial melting of the mantle wedge above subduction zones, Archean crust stemmed from melting of a basaltic source, most probably oceanic crust capping the subducted slab of oceanic lithosphere.

- Lewisian gneisses and Archean shales that represent eroded upper crustal materials, have no europium anomalies. Their post-Archean equivalents commonly have negative europium anomalies, due to fractional crystallization of feldspars from parent magmas to generate post-Archean, upper continental crust.

- The lack of evidence for fractional crystallization in generating Archean crust suggests that it formed from intermediate to felsic magmas, derived by slab melting. Archean crust was probably quartz-rich throughout, unlike the layered crust of later times, whose quartz-free lower layer adds strength to younger lithosphere. Archean continental lithosphere may have been significantly weaker than its later equivalent. Its present rigidity in cratons stems from the loss of heat-producing isotopes by Archean lower crust during high-grade metamorphism, causing very low heat flow through these stable 'shields'.

4.3   Assembly of the Lewisian continent

The original Lewisian crust of the Northern Region formed at 2800 Ma, and underwent wholesale ductile reworking and partial melting in the Laxfordian event at 1750 Ma. It evolved very differently from that of the Central Region, much of which retains structures and mineralogy formed a billion years earlier. Laxfordian deformation in the Central Region involved merely a few narrow shear zones, such as the Canisp Shear Zone (Figure 4.2). After that event the entire Lewisian crust became a craton, on which the Torridonian sediments were eventually laid down around 1000 Ma. During the Laxfordian, the Northern Region was as weak as expected from the bulk composition of Archean crust. Its heat flow must have been considerably higher than that through the Central Region, which has remained cratonic since 2700 Ma. For such different behaviours to have co-existed in two blocks that formed adjacent to each other, is highly unlikely. Figure 4.8 shows the boundary between the two blocks (the Laxford Front) in moderate detail.

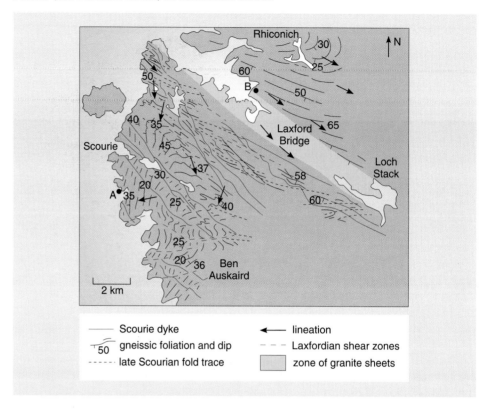

Figure 4.8 Geological map of the boundary between the 2800 Ma Laxfordian gneisses, reworked until 1700 Ma to the north-east, with the anhydrous, 3000-Ma-old Badcallian gneisses that retain all the features of their deep-crustal deformation and metamorphism at 2700 Ma to the south-west. Location shown on Figure 4.2. The main localities visited in the video (*The Lewisian of NW Scotland*) are indicated by A and B.

The nature of the Laxford Front is discussed in Activity 4.1. Its form, and its separation of gneisses with contrasting ages, structural histories and geochemical characteristics, suggest that it may be a terrane boundary. However, it has no associated ophiolites or an accretionary prism, so suggesting that it represents a subduction zone is conjectural. The relationship helps explain some of the smaller structures in the Central Region.

> **Question 4.2** (a) What is the evidence given in Activity 4.1 that small-scale tectonic reworking did affect the deep crustal rocks of the Central Region around 1750 Ma? (b) What may have induced weakening exploited by that reworking?

The Laxford Front is best described as a 'cryptic' suture. The dominance of late strike–slip movements along it (Activity 4.1) could have removed more tangible evidence for a destructive plate boundary. In contrast, the Paleoproterozoic supracrustal complex in the Gairloch area (Section 4.1, Figure 4.2) contains metabasalts, which are geochemically similar to modern ocean-island basalts and those from island arcs. Sediments in the complex include abyssal muds and ironstones produced by ocean-floor hydrothermal activity, and also turbidites that formed from continental debris. Although highly modified by Laxfordian deformation, the Paleoproterozoic supracrustal rocks possibly formed in an accretionary prism associated with subduction. The Gairloch Shear Zone (Figure 4.2) that separates the Central and Southern Regions of the mainland Lewisian is probably another suture, gneisses of the Southern Region having similar ages of formation to those of the Northern Region. Paleoproterozoic rocks in the Hebrides include calc-alkaline igneous intrusions and a variety of high-grade metasediments. They too probably formed in a subduction-zone setting that juxtaposed blocks of Archean crust, represented by the dominant gneisses of the islands. It is difficult to match Lewisian features across the Minch, because of later thrust and strike–slip faulting. Nonetheless, it is clear that the Lewisian Complex is a tectonic collage of several tiny Archean masses that may have been microcontinental slivers before they amalgamated at around 1750 Ma.

The Archean part of the Lewisian Complex, along with other much larger areas of pre-2500 Ma crust, reveals a profound difference in crust-forming processes from those of later times. A look at the way in which the Earth's heat generation has changed with time may help understand that dichotomy, by pointing to changes in its influence on tectonics.

4.3.1 Summary of Section 4.3

- The Lewisian Complex formed from three formerly unrelated masses of Archean continental lithosphere by their tectonic assembly, which involved both collision and strike–slip docking. The Laxford Front is one of the probable sutures at which lithosphere of the Northern and Central Regions met. However, major strike–slip movement along it may have removed any direct evidence for subduction. The Gairloch Shear Zone, which separates the Southern and Central Regions, may be another suture. It adjoins a Paleoproterozoic supracrustal series of metasedimentary and mafic metavolcanic rocks akin to products of an accretionary prism.

4.4 Driving forces for Archean tectonics

Below a depth of a few hundred kilometres, the mantle is sufficiently hot that rock behaves in a ductile manner. Convection that involves ductile deformation transfers radiogenic heat towards the surface. Convective heat transfer is much faster than the dominant thermal conduction of the lithosphere. Temperature in the deep mantle changes with depth along an adiabatic path, and increases far less with depth than it does in the lithosphere (Figure 4.9). That is particularly well shown by continental lithosphere, where the heat-producing isotopes of potassium, uranium and thorium are strongly concentrated in the continental crust, especially in its upper parts. These elements enter evolved felsic magmas because they are highly incompatible in minerals (olivine, pyroxene and plagioclase feldspar) that make up the mantle and oceanic crust, and which crystallize from mafic magmas to leave felsic residual magma during fractional crystallization. Partial melting of subducted oceanic crust or the mantle wedge,

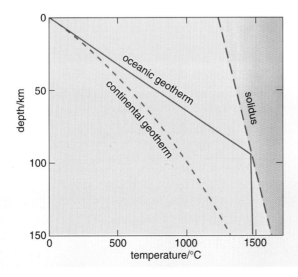

Figure 4.9 Typical geotherms in oceanic and continental lithosphere. Oceanic lithosphere is about 100 km thick, whereas that beneath continents is thicker than 200 km. The solidus is for the mantle.

and fractional crystallization, have progressively added felsic magmas to the continents since the Archean, thereby concentrating K, U and Th in continental crust. These processes have progressively depleted the mantle's heat production, as has radioactive decay of heat-producing isotopes.

Despite the oceanic lithosphere's much lower heat production than that beneath continents, mean heat flow though the ocean floor is 50% greater than through the continental surface (Block 1, Section 2.4). This profound difference demonstrates that at present (and without doubt throughout geological time) the bulk of heat produced in the mantle is lost through the ocean floor. Decompression melting of mantle at constructive margins transfers mafic magmas and heat to the surface. Heat flow through the ocean floor decreases with increasing distance from constructive margins, and thus with the age of oceanic lithosphere. That stems from its cooling by interaction with seawater and heat loss by conduction. The movement of oceanic lithosphere to ultimate resorption into the mantle by subduction is an integral part of convective heat transfer. Continental lithosphere cannot be subducted *en masse*, and new additions cause it to grow continually.

4.4.1   Heat production throughout Earth history

Assessing how heat production varied throughout Earth history depends on estimations of the mantle's changing abundances of heat-producing isotopes. One approach uses the composition of modern basalts, well-known partition coefficients and models for melting and fractional crystallization (Block 2) as a means of estimating mantle composition.

● Which two main difficulties does such an approach face?

● Primary mafic magmas very rarely, if ever, reach the surface. Most mafic lavas show evidence of evolution, thereby complicating back-calculation of mantle composition. Also, it has become clear from studies of mafic magmas emerging in different tectonic settings that the modern mantle is not homogeneous in composition (Block 2).

Mantle heterogeneity has probably arisen from past melting events, most clearly shown by the incompatible-element depleted source of mid-ocean ridge basalts (including U, Th and K), compared with that giving rise to basalts associated with plumes. Another approach assumes that the Earth formed by accretion of the most primitive, chondritic meteorites and inherited a geochemical 'signature' from them. That too has its imponderables, not the least of which being that a huge impact spewed off matter to form the Moon shortly after the Earth had accreted. Such a titanic event probably left the outer Earth as a magma ocean that rapidly cooled and crystallized, and must surely have modified Earth's bulk composition.

Bearing those difficulties in mind, the simplest approach to the evolution of the Earth's heat production is to assume a chondritic bulk composition. The chondritic abundances of K, U and Th, together with the decay constants and heat production per kilogram of their unstable isotopes, provide the means to estimate how each isotope has contributed to heat production through geological time (Figure 4.10).

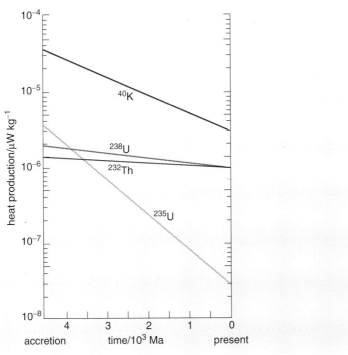

Figure 4.10 Plots of heat production through time for the isotopes of K, U and Th, assuming a chondritic bulk Earth. Heat production is expressed as microwatts per kilogram of rock equivalent to the bulk Earth. Note that the heat-production axis is logarithmic to encompass large variations, which results in exponential declines in abundance of decaying isotopes appearing as straight lines.

Question 4.3 (a) How has the order of importance of the four heat-producing isotopes changed with time? (b) Construct a plot of how total heat production has varied, by choosing three times (every 2000 Ma since the origin of the Earth), reading off the heat production for each isotope and then adding the four values. (c) Which of the estimates of abundance is most critical in assessing past heat production?

The plot that you drew in Question 4.3 is a rough guide to how the Earth's internal activity has decreased in its intensity through geological time.

Question 4.4 The major 'milestones' in Earth's evolution are at 4000 Ma (the oldest-known rocks), 2500 Ma (the end of the Archean Eon) and 540 Ma (the start of the Phanerozoic Eon and the fossil record). At each point, how many times greater was radiogenic heat production than it is now, based on the assumption of a chondritic composition for the bulk Earth?

As you should expect from the exponential decay of unstable isotopes, any model of the Earth's internal heat production results in a rapid increase going back in time. However, the chondritic model probably overestimates the contribution of ^{40}K. Moreover, heat generated and retained by accretion of the Earth and core formation has almost certainly contributed to heat throughout geological time. Figure 4.11a is an estimate based on these factors. From it stems Figure 4.11b, the variation in estimated mean surface heat flow. Together, these two Figures allow you to assess the effects of changing heat production on several aspects of the Earth's behaviour.

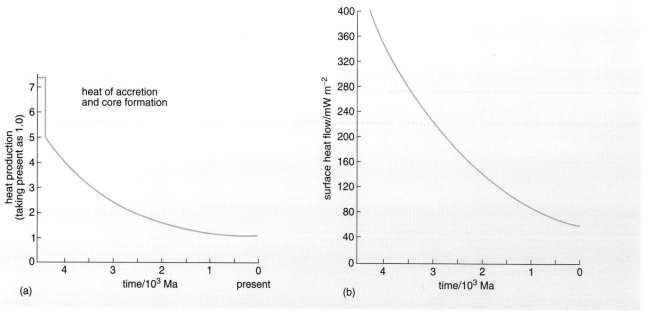

Figure 4.11 (a) Variation in the Earth's heat production, assuming addition of heat in its earliest stages by accretion, origin of the Moon by a giant impact on the Earth and core formation. For most of its history, internal heat production has been dominated by decaying radioactivity. Modern heat production has an arbitrary value of 1.0. (b) Estimated variation in mean surface heat flow since about 4400 Ma. Note that the vertical axes are linear in both (a) and (b).

One factor that does not show on Figure 4.11, yet must have delivered considerable heat to the Earth's interior, is the effect of impacts other than that which probably induced Moon formation. By analogy with the Moon's impact history, the Earth must have been struck by as many as 50 objects that excavated craters more than 1000 km in diameter at the time of the events that created the Moon's *maria*. That **late heavy bombardment** spanned the period from about 4100 to 3800 Ma ago. It had a profound effect on the Moon — the *maria*, up to 2000 km across, are floored by mafic magma generated by partial melting of the lunar mantle — and similar events on Earth would have been even more dramatic.

In terms of power (energy delivered per second), such impacts dwarf radiogenic heat production, albeit for short periods. An impact that excavated a structure 1000 km across — that would have taken around a second — would have delivered about 3×10^{27} W. For the Earth's mass of 6×10^{24} kg, that amounts to 500 W kg^{-1}, about 10 trillion (10^{13}) times more than the power of Earth's heat production 4000 Ma ago. The biggest likely impact structure formed on Earth at that time, about 6000 km across, would have involved 8 kW kg^{-1}. The power of a 1000-km-wide impact is equivalent to radiogenic heat production at 4000 Ma rates for 1.2×10^{13} seconds, or about half a million years. Clearly, such impacts would have had global consequences, because the extra heat would have to be dissipated in some way, almost certainly by increased partial melting. However, no impact structures from the late heavy bombardment remain to be seen: subsequent geological processes have either removed or hidden them. The near certainty of the influence of giant impacts on the earliest period of geological history has spurred geologists to look for secondary signs in Archean sequences. At the time of writing (2002), they have discovered two clear signs: (i) glass spherules and high noble-metal contents in thin sedimentary layers within 3600 Ma supracrustal rocks in Swaziland and Western Australia; (ii) tungsten isotopes in 3800 Ma supracrustal rocks from West Greenland (Section 4.5.1) that show the influence of extraterrestrial material.

- Bearing in mind the nature of impacts, what manner of magmatism would they probably set in motion?

- Falling at points on the Earth's surface, impacts would probably generate partial melting very like that associated with mantle plumes, particularly those that begin to melt at shallow depths (Block 2, Section 5).

The elusiveness of impact structures from the late heavy bombardment renders their role in Earth evolution something to be borne in mind rather than pursued here. Fascinating as they are for biological evolution, later known impact structures show no direct evidence of having influenced global tectonics.

4.4.2 Has there always been plate tectonics?

Block 1, Section 2.3 dealt with the relationship between heat flow and the temperature gradient within the lithosphere where movement of heat is by conduction.

- Why is the lithosphere a zone where heat is conducted rather than convected?

- It behaves as a rigid plate most of the time, and so convection is not possible.

- If there is an increase in heat flow though the lithosphere, what happens to the temperature gradient in it?

- It increases.

Different heat flows therefore support different geotherms, as shown in Block 1, Figure 2.1. Three fundamental processes change in some way according to heat flow: metamorphism; partial melting; and rheological behaviour of the lithosphere. Changes at subduction zones are especially important.

Figure 4.12 shows the variation of temperature with depth along a modern subduction zone in relation to the conditions for both metamorphism and partial melting of downgoing oceanic crust — the upper part of the subducted slab. You will recall that by the time oceanic crust reaches a destructive plate margin, it has cooled, and it contains hydrous minerals formed by reaction with seawater.

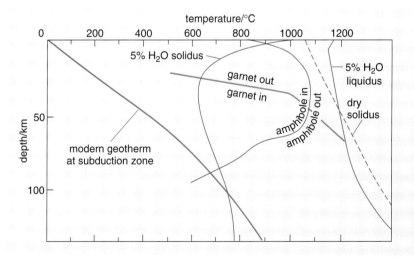

Figure 4.12 *P–T* diagram showing changes in temperature with depth in a subducted slab of oceanic lithosphere (see Block 3, Figure 2.12b) in relation to the stability limits of amphibole and garnet in oceanic basalt, and to the solidus and liquidus for hydrous basalt. The solidus for dry basalt appears as a dashed line.

● What are the main conclusions that you can draw from Figure 4.12 about metamorphic and igneous processes at modern subduction zones?

● First, the slab-temperature plot crosses the line defining conditions for dehydration of amphibole at a shallower depth than it crosses the 'wet' basalt solidus. This implies that modern subduction generally dries out the descending oceanic crust, so that it becomes less likely to undergo partial melting deeper down. Water rising from this zone of dehydration also carries heat, and the two help induce the overlying mantle wedge to undergo partial melting. That explains the dominance of basaltic magmas that add to volcanic arcs and unique aspects of their geochemistry (Block 3, Section 3). The second important conclusion arises from the modern slab-temperature plot falling in the field of garnet stability. Together with dehydration of amphiboles, garnet formation in the oceanic crust contributes to its transformation to garnet pyroxene-bearing rock (eclogite). This has a greater density than the surrounding mantle peridotite, and contributes to the sinking of the subducted slab at a steep angle.

Question 4.5 Sketch onto Figure 4.12 a slab geotherm associated with a higher heat flow at a destructive margin. What might be the consequences of higher heat flow at subduction zones for dehydration of amphibole in relation to partial melting of wet basalt?

The answer to Question 4.5 suggests that earlier in geological history the production of magma at destructive margins could have been profoundly different from today. Your discovery in Section 4.2 of geochemical evidence for widespread slab melting during the Archean matches geothermal theory.

Another issue is whether **eclogite** has always formed from subducted oceanic crust. Eclogite is an anhydrous rock composed of garnet and pyroxene that forms by high-pressure metamorphism of cold basalt. Wet oceanic crust at modern destructive margins that follows the slab geotherm shown in Figure 4.12 begins to dehydrate once it crosses the stability curve for amphibole. It then becomes eclogite, whose density ($3300 \, kg \, m^{-3}$) is greater than that of mantle peridotite ($3100 \, kg \, m^{-3}$).

Experimental metamorphism of anhydrous basalt shows that for pressures lower than those along the garnet in–garnet out line on Figure 4.12, plagioclase and pyroxene are stable. At higher pressures, a mixture of plagioclase, pyroxene and garnet becomes stable, corresponding to garnet granulite. At the highest pressures, the stable minerals are just garnet and pyroxene, i.e. eclogite. Figure 4.13 shows the fields of these three mineral assemblages in anhydrous basalt. Garnet is a dense mineral, but it is not the sole reason for the unusually high density of eclogite. The components of plagioclase and pyroxene (Al, Fe, Mg and Ca, with silica) contribute to garnet growth at intermediate pressures. However, none of the sodium and not all the calcium in feldspar can enter the garnet molecule, so that plagioclase remains stable in garnet granulites. The disappearance of feldspar at higher pressures occurs because a high-pressure pyroxene called omphacite consumes all the remaining elements that garnet cannot accommodate. It is the mixture of garnet and omphacite that makes eclogite denser than the mantle. While feldspar remains stable in metamorphosed basalt, oceanic lithosphere is unable to sink into the mantle (garnet granulite has a density of around $3000 \, kg \, m^{-3}$).

● What is the influence of eclogite over modern plate tectonics as a whole?

● The sinking of dense oceanic lithosphere imparts slab–pull force to tectonics — by far the largest influence on the movement of plates (Block 1, Section 1.3) — and this results in steep subduction.

Arguably, without slab–pull, there would be no subduction, and it is difficult to envisage plate tectonics without it. If at some time in the past heat flow was too great to allow basalt to transform to eclogite, slab–pull force would not assist motions of the oceanic lithosphere. Quite possibly, tectonics before that time would have been very different from that which operates now. Assessing such a possibility depends on evidence for the oldest formation of eclogite and on examining the stability field of eclogite in $P–T$ space in relation to likely subduction-zone slab-temperature plots during the Archean. The oldest-known eclogites (around 3100 Ma) occur as inclusions in Phanerozoic diamond-bearing kimberlite pipes that cut the Archean of Southern Africa. Because they come from beneath continental crust that achieved very low heat production during the earlier Archean (in much the same manner as the Central Region of the Lewisian), they probably did not form in an Archean subduction zone but in the cold lithospheric 'root' of that very old craton. Figure 4.13 shows the stability fields of gabbro, garnet granulite and eclogite in relation to features shown in Figure 4.12.

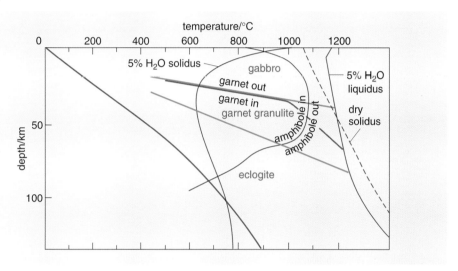

Figure 4.13 As Figure 4.12, with the addition of the stability fields of gabbro, garnet granulite and eclogite.

By how much would the slab temperature at all depths need to increase for basalt not to enter the eclogite field?

It would need to increase by a little less than a factor of 2.

This would be possible with a doubling of heat flow beneath subduction zones, and Figure 4.11b shows that about 1750 Ma ago the Earth's mean heat flow would have been double that at present. So, from this very simple standpoint, it might seem that slab–pull force may well not have operated in the Archean and Paleoproterozoic. However, variation of slab temperature with depth is not just a product of heat flow at destructive margins. It depends on the rate of subduction and the temperature of the slab when it starts to be subducted. Clearly, Earth scientists need another approach to the vital issue of how long slab–pull has operated.

4.4.3 Changing rates of sea-floor spreading

The bulk of the Earth's heat production emerges at constructive margins (and to a lesser extent through hot spots). Slow cooling of magma newly added to the oceanic lithosphere dissipates heat through the oceans and ultimately to outer space. As oceans spread, so the lithosphere cools in a fairly systematic manner outwards from the ridge system (Block 1, Figure 2.3). The older the oceanic lithosphere, the cooler and more dense it becomes, and the deeper the ocean floor. This being the case, greater heat production in the past implies commensurately greater production of magmas generated by partial melting of the mantle. The rise of this magma to form oceanic lithosphere would have dissipated the additional heat as today, only more quickly.

There are three possibilities that stem logically from this need to lose heat faster:

1   for a similar number of plates to those present today, the overall rate of sea-floor spreading would have been greater; and/or

2   for the same spreading rates as occur now there would have been more plates, and they would have been smaller; and/or

3   sea-floor spreading was similar to present behaviour, but a greater proportion of heat production emerged through plume-related volcanism, i.e. at hot spots.

⬤   What do the first two possibilities imply for the P–T variation in subducting plates?

⬤   Faster spreading would have resulted in less cooling of the oceanic lithosphere by the time it reached a subduction zone. The same outcome arises from the second possibility, but that would have been because young material would have less far to go in arriving at a subduction zone.

The same outcome from both possible changes in sea-floor spreading suggests that, on average, younger and warmer oceanic lithosphere would have entered subduction zones in earlier times. To judge whether this might at any time have changed the nature of subduction significantly, you need to assess just how young and just how warm the slab might have been.

The oldest oceanic lithosphere on the floor of modern ocean basins is about 170 Ma old, but the average age of subducting lithosphere is roughly 80 Ma. Figure 4.14 shows how heat flow through oceanic lithosphere decreases with increasing age away from spreading centres. Crudely speaking, heat flow through modern subducting slabs averages about 50 mW m^{-2}.

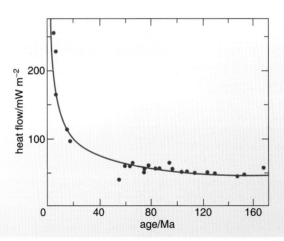

Figure 4.14 Variation in heat flow with age for modern oceanic lithosphere.

Question 4.6 This question relies on two assumptions. The first is that the age at which oceanic lithosphere enters subduction zones is on average inversely proportional to the rate of sea-floor spreading, and therefore to the Earth's heat production (see Figure 4.11a). The second is that the average temperature of oceanic crust that is about to be subducted is directly proportional to the heat flow through it. Both are likely to be approximately true. Slabs entering subduction with a heat flow appropriate for an average age of 80 Ma today have the P–T structure shown in Figure 4.13. (a) What is the minimum age of modern lithosphere that would fail to become eclogite? (b) At what time in the past would you expect all subducted basalt in lithosphere to fail to become eclogite?

Crude as this approach is, it suggests that plate tectonics assisted by slab–pull from oceanic lithosphere made dense by the basalt–eclogite transition probably occurred throughout the whole of recorded geological time. The accretionary complex in the oldest volcanic–sedimentary association on Earth, at Isua in West Greenland (Section 4.5.1), is evidence for plate tectonics and some form of subduction. However, even today there are cases of shallow-angled subduction, the largest being beneath the Andes of Peru (Block 3, Figure 7.6), where eclogite probably does not form. Moreover, you have already seen in Section 4.2 that Archean oceanic lithosphere, principally the oceanic crust, failed to dehydrate before crossing the 'wet' basalt solidus, and thereby generated felsic magmas by partially melting in subduction zones. (Block 3 Box 7.1 describes felsic magmas, or adakites, that form by slab melting along modern, low-angle subduction zones; adakites may be analogous to magmas that formed Archean continental crust.) Crystallization of these magmas to form the early continental crust imparted low strength to the Archean continental lithosphere. The end of the Archean represents a fundamental time boundary as regards the Earth's internal processes. Before that boundary, tectonics was very different from that of later times.

In the next two Sections, you will see first how lower continental strength and its response to lithospheric stress can help explain some structural features of the Archean part of the Lewisian, and then how a few peculiar features in much larger cratons fit with your review of ancient geothermal processes and amplify the alien nature of the Archean world.

4.4.4 Summary of Section 4.4

• Assuming that the composition of the bulk Earth is similar to that of chondritic meteorites, exponential decay of the heat-producing isotopes of potassium, uranium and thorium suggests that total heat production was between 10 and 4 times greater than at present when the first continental rocks formed 4000 Ma ago and at the end of the Archean (2500 Ma) respectively. The greatest uncertainties in such estimates are the contribution of ^{40}K, because some potassium may have been lost at the time of Moon formation, and the amount of heat retained from that event, and from initial accretion and core formation. These factors all contribute to estimating the variation of heat flow over geological time. Another important factor is the occasional contribution of heat by very high-powered impacts in the past, the largest such extraterrestrial heat delivery having been between 4100 and 3800 Ma (the late heavy bombardment).

• Higher heat flow in the past would have affected the depth and amount of partial melting, the mineralogy of subducted oceanic lithosphere, and strength of the lithosphere. At destructive plate margins, the type of metamorphism of the subducted slab, and the potential for partial melting to take place within it or in the overlying mantle wedge, depend to a large degree on the temperature of the oceanic lithosphere when it reaches a subduction zone. Higher heat production may have speeded up the average rate of sea-floor spreading, resulted in a greater number of smaller plates than now, or both. In either case, younger, and therefore warmer lithosphere would have reached subduction zones than happens now. If the temperature of the slab exceeded that of the 'wet' basalt solidus at lower pressures than the dehydration temperature of amphiboles, the basaltic part of the slab must have begun to partially melt. Since all analysed Archean felsic materials show that slab melting did happen, such conditions applied globally before 2500 Ma ago. Modern adakites (Block 3) may be rare analogues of Archean subduction zone magmas.

- The formation of dense eclogite from basalt in the subducted slab is today a major reason for both steep subduction and slab–pull force. If subducted slabs followed a pressure–temperature path that failed to enter the field of eclogite stability, because their temperature was above a threshold value, tectonics would have been very different from today. A doubling of average heat flow beneath oceans, estimated to have been the case before 1750 Ma ago, would have that effect. However, simple calculations suggest that total heat production would need to have been four times the present value for such a change to affect the entire oceanic lithosphere. That would have been the case before 4000 Ma ago, based on the conservative estimates of heat production in the past. But the fact that low-angled subduction, probably without eclogite formation, does take place today suggests that in the Archean it would have been a more common attribute of global tectonics.

4.5 Signs of Archean tectonics

Occurrences of Archean rocks in the great cratons, around which later continental crust has grown, take on two general forms: (i) vast tracts of gneisses formed in much the same manner as the Lewisian by high-grade metamorphism and pervasive ductile deformation — Archean **high-grade complexes**; and (ii) lower-grade tracts consisting of basins filled by sedimentary and volcanic rocks, in which many original features of Archean surface processes remain, together with older gneisses and abundant granitic plutons — **granite–greenstone complexes**. The term 'greenstone' refers to the common green tinge of unweathered mafic volcanic rocks that contain abundant green chlorite and epidote formed by low-grade metamorphism.

(*Note*: We do not expect you to remember details from this Section, just the broad conclusions that can be drawn from the rocks and the structures that they show.)

4.5.1 The Archean high-grade complex of West Greenland

When the Greenland ice cap retreated in the last few thousand years, it uncovered near-perfect occurrences of Archean rocks near Nuuk (formerly Godthaab) in West Greenland, which have become famous through intensive study. For 30 years they included the oldest-known rocks in the world (3800 Ma). The Akasta gneisses of northern Canada now have that distinction and are close to 4000 Ma old. The Nuuk area does preserve the most ancient examples of sedimentary and volcanic rocks. It exposes three Archean terranes, each of which was highly deformed when they assembled between 2700 and 2800 Ma ago (Figure 4.15). The first of these, the Akulleq terrane, contains two suites of rocks between 3700 and 3800 Ma old: the Amîtsoq gneisses, which resemble the Lewisian, and formed from tonalitic to granodiorite plutons; and the Akilia Association of high-grade sediments, volcanics and fragments of mantle materials, aged around 3800 Ma, which are tectonically interleaved with Amîtsoq gneisses.

The Akilia Association is very diverse, containing coarse ultramafic and mafic igneous rocks, basaltic pillow lavas, manganese-rich breccias derived from the lavas, interbedded cherts and banded iron formation (BIF), carbonates, various

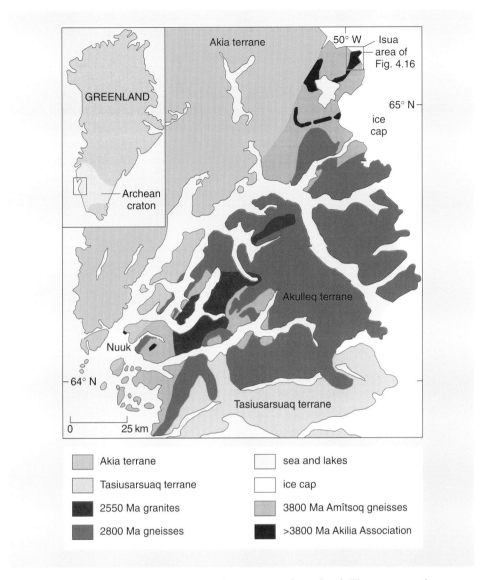

Figure 4.15 Outline geology of the Nuuk area, West Greenland. The map greatly simplifies two of the Archean terranes: the northern Akia terrane (3000–3200 Ma) in light brown, and the southern Tasiusarsuaq terrane (2800–2900 Ma). The central Akulleq terrane has four different components (as shown in the key). The oldest materials are sedimentary, volcanic and mantle rocks, dated at >3800 Ma, known as the Akilia Association. The largest occurrence of them is in the Isua area, at the NE corner of the map. These supracrustal rocks are enveloped by gneisses (~3800 Ma old), known as the Amîtsoq gneisses. A younger (2800 Ma) gneiss complex and the Amîtsoq gneisses were cut by an undeformed granite mass at 2550 Ma (the oldest-known true granite). The small rectangle in the NE corner of the map shows the Isua area of Akilia supracrustal rocks detailed in Figure 4.16.

turbidites and, in one part, a mélange (Activity 5.1) consisting of blocks and fragments of all these lithologies set in a muddy matrix. The best-preserved occurrence of these supracrustal rocks is close to the Greenland ice sheet, at a place called Isua (Figure 4.16).

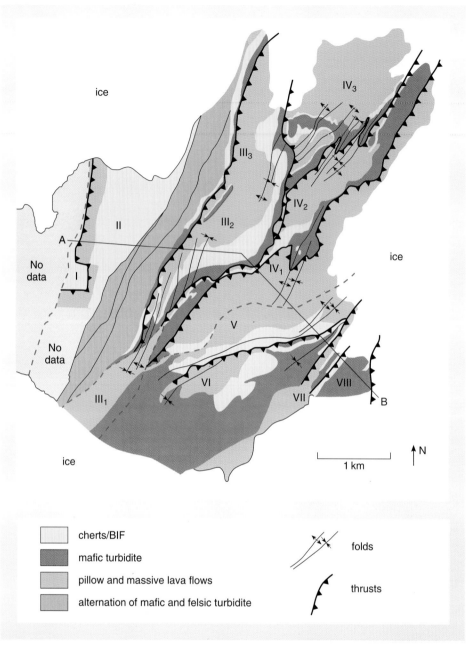

Figure 4.16 Simplified geological map of part of the Isua area, West Greenland. See inset key for colours signifying the important rock groups. Small occurrences of ultramafic rocks and carbonate sediments have been omitted for clarity. Dip of the bedding is consistently towards the SE, at between 40 and 70°, and pillows in the basaltic unit indicate that all strata are right-way-up. The toothed black lines are thrust faults almost parallel to the bedding in the supracrustal rocks of the Akilia Association — they too dip consistently to the SE. Both branching of the faults, and folds younger than the faulting (axial traces shown as fine lines with antiform and synform symbols), have created the complexity in this area. The thrusts divide the geology into eight fault-bounded blocks, labelled I to VIII. Line A–B is the section line shown in Figure 4.17. The dashed red lines are later normal faults.

The strata shown in Figure 4.16 are the right way up, and dip consistently at moderate to steep angles to the SE, so it is possible to deduce the stratigraphic succession in each of the thrust-bound blocks. From NW to SE in Block III_3, the outcrops change from pillow lavas, to cherts with BIFs, to mafic sediments.

Because the dip is towards the SE, this sequence is in order of decreasing stratigraphic age — lavas are the oldest and mafic sediments are the youngest. All the blocks show this general sequence, but variations in outcrop width signify variations in thickness from block to block. Block II is the only one in which there is a substantial thickness of quartz-rich, clastic sediments (felsic turbidites). Faults separate the blocks, and the consistent sense of stratigraphic repetition across all the faults shows that each of them is a thrust. Figure 4.17 shows a simple sequence of thrust-bound blocks. The overall structure is that of a thrust duplex.

- You encountered similar thrust duplexes in Block 3. What is the most likely origin of that at Isua?

- It is almost certainly an accretionary prism, particularly because each block consists of rocks that seem to have affinities with oceanic crust.

- Assuming that is the case, suggest the sequence in which each block became accreted. Which block would have been furthest from the subduction system when the process began?

- Because materials are added to the accretionary prism at its leading, oceanward edge, additions become progressively younger away from the arc. This implies that accretionary prisms tend to grow oceanwards. Block VIII was the earliest to accrete and Block I the last. It follows that Block I would have been furthest out in the ocean, when the arc system began to form.

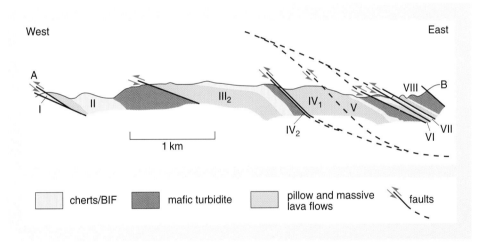

Figure 4.17 Structural cross-section along line A–B on Figure 4.16. It shows repetition of an upward lava–chert/BIF–turbidite succession in a thrust duplex. Note the varying thickness of the chert/BIF and turbidite units from block to block.

The sequence in the lower part of each block (pillow lavas and cherts) has the hallmarks of ocean floor, followed by stratigraphically younger turbidites. Examining detailed stratigraphic sequences from the structural blocks allows a deeper insight into their evolution relative to one another (Figure 4.18).

Different thicknesses of cherts accumulated in the different blocks. Chert signifies deposition in an environment starved of clastic debris, on the deep ocean floor. Assuming a constant rain of whatever contributed to chert build-up, the thicker a chert unit, the longer it took to accumulate. Therefore, increasing chert thickness might signify increasing age away from a spreading centre that generated the oceanic lithosphere on which the chert rests.

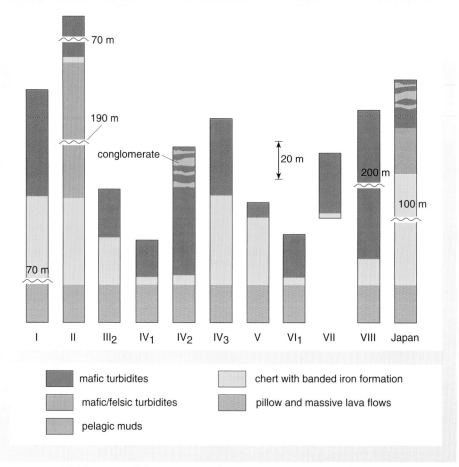

Figure 4.18 Thicknesses of the various sedimentary units in each of the fault-bounded blocks at Isua. The blocks' inferred age of accretion increases from right to left. No thickness is assigned to the lavas, because their base is never exposed. Note that some layers in some blocks are much thicker than the figure permits — signified by wavy lines interrupting the layer and a thickness for the omitted material. For comparison, the log at far right is from a Mesozoic ophiolite in Japan.

The upper turbidites contain clastic materials, and indicate that ocean floor became close to an area undergoing erosion that must have risen relative to the level of the ocean floor, thereby becoming a source of granular sediment. Fine-grained clastics (pelagic muds) in the Mesozoic ophiolite signify clastic sedimentation at a greater distance from its source than do turbidites and conglomerates. The Isua sediments contain no such material. Mafic turbidites suggest a source of sediment was made predominantly of oceanic lithosphere that had somehow been uplifted, whereas felsic debris implies a source in an island arc with evolved igneous rocks.

The Isua duplex is exactly what you would expect to find in a modern accretionary prism, despite being 3800 Ma old, and therefore does imply Archean plate tectonics. The authors of the Isua study developed a plate-tectonic model for the formation of the Amîtsoq gneisses, which are structurally mixed with supracrustal rocks of the Akilia Association (Figure 4.19). The tonalite to granodiorite Amîtsoq gneisses formed in an island arc by partial melting of the subducted slab of oceanic crust (Section 4.2.1). The absence of pelagic muds from the Isua blocks compared with their usual occurrence in Phanerozoic ophiolites might signify more rapid early Archean plate movements, as anticipated from geothermal considerations (Section 4.4.3).

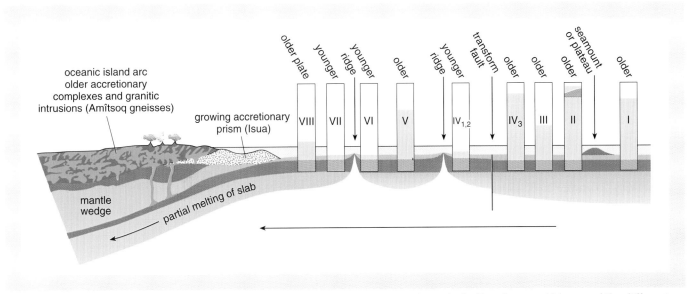

Figure 4.19 Tectonic interpretation of the Akilia Association and Amîtsoq gneisses, including the travel history of the different blocks in the Isua thrust duplex. The various ridges, transform faults and seamounts or plateaux, and the positions relative to them of blocks I to VIII, are inferred from the different thicknesses of cherts (yellow) in each block. Thinner cherts in VII and VI than in VIII and V suggest the position of one spreading ridge that was subducted. A second ridge is inferred from thin cherts of blocks IV$_{1,2}$. The felsic turbidites in block II are assumed to have been derived from volcanism at an oceanic island, because they are capped by cherts, suggesting volcanism ended while block II was still far from the site of its eventual accretion. The difference in chert thicknesses in I to IV$_3$ from that in IV$_{1,2}$ could imply that oceanic lithosphere with different age patterns had been juxtaposed to that to the left along a transform fault.

Supracrustal sequences intricately interleaved with tonalitic to granodioritic gneisses are common in younger, high-grade Archean complexes, but early structures in them are 'scrambled' by later events. The mafic granulites associated with Lewisian supracrustal rocks (Activity 4.1) have chemical similarities to the Isua pillow lavas and to modern ocean-floor basalts. The Lewisian green quartzites may well have formed as oceanic cherts, whereas staurolite- and kyanite-bearing metasediments are possible candidates for pelagic muds (Activity 4.1). Indeed, the many other varieties of Lewisian metasediments (ironstones, marbles and possible metaturbidites) can all be matched to analogues in an accretionary prism. The Lewisian mafic–ultramafic complexes may be cumulates from the base of oceanic crust. However, intense deformation and metamorphism has discouraged geologists working on the Lewisian from drawing such a conclusion. Most Archean high-grade complexes probably formed by thickening of island-arc crust at early subduction zones. In low-grade Archean terranes, that resemblance to modern tectonics ends.

4.5.2 Archean granite–greenstone complexes

Satellite images of Archean granite–greenstone complexes (Figure 4.20) that cover areas far larger than Scotland or West Greenland show features very different from younger crust. Post-Archean orogens are much narrower than they are long. The Himalaya and Tibetan Plateau (Block 4) juxtapose older continents that 'trap' intervening volcanic arcs, accretionary prisms and a variety of sedimentary basins. The Phanerozoic orogen of western North America (Block 1, Figure 1.15) is one-sided, being the outcome of successive accretion of exotic material to one margin of an ocean. Archean patterns are dominated by many narrow greenstone belts enveloped by broad areas of gneisses and later granitic plutons. Most greenstone-belt sequences in such an area have similar ages and contents. Many rest unconformably on higher-grade gneisses, which have roughly uniform, though older, ages. Such greenstone belts formed on earlier continental crust, and cannot represent island arcs. However, they contain immense thicknesses of volcanic and sedimentary rocks, that suggest rapid subsidence of the basins in which they formed. Their tectonic setting involved widespread extension of Archean continental lithosphere. They also show few signs of subaerial deposition, unlike the contents of younger continental basins. Most of the volcanic rocks within them show features, such as pillows that lack gas bubbles, which indicate extrusion in deep water. Their sediments are dominantly turbidites, with shallower-water carbonates and banded ironstone formations.

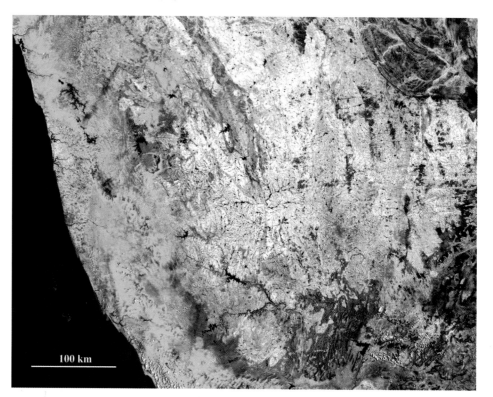

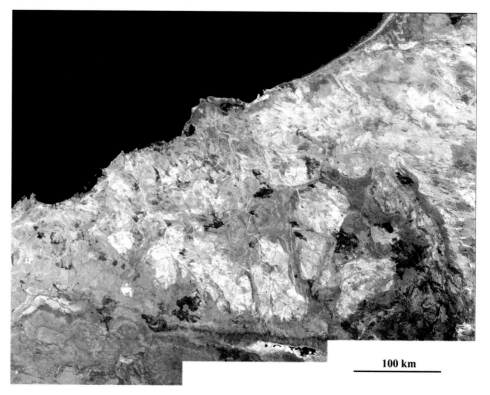

Figure 4.20 Satellite images showing sedimentary–volcanic greenstone belts (dark) set in a gneissic and granitic 'sea' in Archean cratons of (a) southern India and (b) western Australia.

Not all granite-greenstone complexes formed directly on earlier crust. Detailed mapping of several Canadian complexes shows convincing evidence that they formed by lateral tectonics, involving accretion at destructive margins of ocean floor materials. Volcanic rocks in these greenstone belts include basalts with affinities to ocean plateaux formed above hot spots, and oceanic island arcs. Those examples, as at Isua, show no reason to depart from uniformitarian ideas, modified to take account of a more dynamic Archean Earth with higher heat production. However, vast areas of Archean India, southern Africa and western Australia (Figure 4.20) possess greenstone belts that formed within older Archean continents. A uniformitarian outlook accounts for that by proposing that such examples either hide evidence for accretionary plate tectonics by their structural complexity, or that the greenstones have been emplaced tectonically upon earlier crust. Some greenstone belts in southern Africa do indeed lie above major detachments (originally mapped as unconformities), and seem to be far-travelled masses, but many more show no such relationships and show clear evidence for extensional tectonics early in their history.

The volcanic rocks of greenstone belts are geochemically very different from those associated with modern ocean floor and volcanic arcs. They do not contain the typical sequences seen in ophiolites, and show no evolutionary trend that can be explained by the processes discussed in Block 3. Greenstone-belt volcanic sequences comprise mafic (and ultramafic) lavas and felsic ones, but contain no andesites. They are bimodal, rather than showing a geochemical 'spectrum' from primitive to highly evolved compositions. The strangest Archean volcanics are those of ultramafic composition, with MgO contents around 25 to 30%. Magnesian basalts (MgO around 14–18%) form in modern arc settings, but they are very rare. Archean examples are volumetrically common, and include compositions very close to peridotite. Archean ultramafic lavas show intricate textures that prove they formed by cooling from a liquid — they cannot be cumulates. Experiments show that the lavas emerged at temperatures far higher than those of basalts; up to 1650 °C in the case of the most magnesian examples.

- What do the high eruption temperatures and high MgO contents of Archean ultramafic lavas imply?

- Lava temperature is a guide to the potential temperature of the mantle (Block 2, Section 3.4.3) from which the parent magma melted, so the source of ultramafic lavas was a great deal hotter than that of basalts. A magma's Mg number (Mg#) (Block 2, Section 2.5.1) reflects the degree to which it has evolved from its primary source, and that of a primary magma signifies the degree of partial melting of mantle peridotite that generated it. Ultramafic lavas are the most unevolved that are known, and must have originated by much higher degrees of partial melting than those that create basaltic magmas.

Because assemblages such as that at Isua, and in some younger greenstones, are dominated by basalts and are free of ultramafic lavas, some Archean basalt magma formed at constructive plate margins by partial melting of asthenosphere that rose during extension, as it does today. Large volumes of ultramafic lavas in some greenstone belts suggest partial melting of mantle from a much deeper source, involving large-scale plume activity.

- What were the products of mantle plumes throughout the Phanerozoic?

- Flood basalts on continents (Deccan), oceanic plateaux (Ontong–Java) and ocean island basalts (Hawaii) (Block 2).

As well as erupting in large volumes at unusually high temperatures, Archean ultramafic lavas are commonly depleted in niobium (Nb), and they also contain zircons.

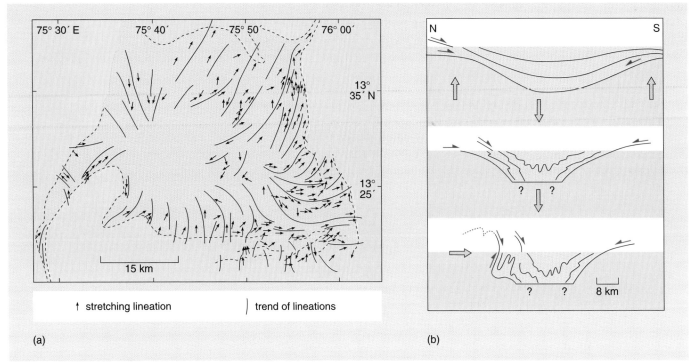

Figure 4.21 (a) Stretching lineations and their general trends in a south Indian greenstone belt. (b) Model for the evolution of the greenstone belt that involves initial formation of a sedimentary–volcanic basin and the gravitational collapse of its dense contents toward the axis, where sinking was at a maximum, with final compressional deformation (from top to bottom).

⬤ Can you suggest how these two features might have originated (see Block 3)?

⬤ Both are evidence for significant contamination by continental crust.

Occurring in extensional basins developed on older crust, the ultramafic lavas passed through the deep continental crust. Such lavas, and the less magnesian basalts that accompany them in greenstone belts, are possibly the equivalents of Phanerozoic continental flood basalts. Yet they generally show evidence of eruption beneath water, and are interleaved and covered by subaqueous sediments of many kinds.

> **Question 4.7** Suggest up to four plausible processes that might explain the formation of greenstone belts on older continental crust and yet beneath water. (*Hint:* density is relevant to each of them.)

Detailed structural analysis of a late-Archean greenstone belt in India, which undoubtedly formed on top of older crust, reveals extraordinary patterns (Figure 4.21). Archean cratons of south India, western Australia and southern Africa have basin-like greenstone belts with intricate cuspate outlines, sometimes taking on 'star' shapes (Figure 4.20), and the older crustal rocks between them occur in domes. The plunges of early stretching lineations in the south Indian greenstone belt, shown in Figure 4.21a, trend radially towards the central part of the belt. Large folds in the belt have axes with a similar radial orientation. The authors of the study concluded that these patterns demonstrate gravitational sagging of the basin in which the greenstone belt evolved (Figure 4.21b). Though controversial, this study suggests that high-density rocks in some Archean greenstone belts, combined with thinner, more ductile crust, could have induced a form of vertical tectonics, unique to the Archean.

General features of magmatism and tectonics since about 4000 Ma suggest that global processes evolved, rather than always being like modern plate tectonics. In the earliest times, lateral and vertical tectonics, driven respectively by sea-floor spreading and mantle plumes, may have had similar importance. Today, plate tectonics dominates. Rather than confirming uniformitarianism — 'the present is the key to the past' — Archean geology suggests that the past gave rise to the present.

4.5.3 Summary of Section 4.5

- Occurrences of Archean rocks are of two general kinds: high-grade and granite–greenstone complexes. The first is highly deformed and metamorphosed, whereas the second preserves original features of sedimentation and volcanic activity.

- Many Archean high-grade complexes evidently formed at destructive margins. Supracrustal rocks in them, if decipherable, closely resemble Phanerozoic accretionary prisms, yet omit pelagic muds and may evidence faster sea-floor spreading. Minor metasediments and mafic–ultramafic bodies in the deep-crustal Lewisian have compositions that are compatible with such a model. The more voluminous gneisses formed by partial melting of subducted oceanic crust, rather than the overlying mantle wedge.

- Some granite–greenstone complexes are structurally different from post-Archean orogenic belts. Their greenstone belts are typically star-shaped, and formed at the same time across entire Archean cratons. Between them are dome-like masses of older felsic gneisses and large intrusions of younger granitic rocks. Structural evidence suggests that the two kinds of structure formed by vertical tectonics, in which thick, high-density mafic to ultramafic lavas induced regional sagging of the crust, while low-density felsic material rose to form domes. Other granite–greenstone complexes seem to have formed at destructive margins, in a similar way to Archean high-grade complexes.

- Magnesium-rich lavas in greenstone belts may have originated by partial melting in mantle plumes in an analogous way to younger flood basalts.

4.6   Implications for Archean tectonics

During the oldest Lewisian metamorphism, ductile deformation in the horizontal plane formed the low-angled structures of the deep-crustal gneisses by immense extension and flattening of the primary compositional banding and the rafts of mafic–ultramafic rocks (Activity 4.1). Mixed in with the gneisses (originally plutonic igneous rocks formed by slab melting) are metasedimentary rocks deposited at the Earth's surface. Although an environment of extreme extension could mix deep-crustal and supracrustal rocks — the favoured model in the video — the interleaving could equally have resulted from compressional tectonics and crustal thickening. However, the present structure of the Badcallian gneisses does indicate that during the 2700 Ma orogeny, the crust extended dramatically.

Crustal extension formed sedimentary basins during the Phanerozoic, such as the North Sea during the Mesozoic and the Basin and Range Province (Block 1, Activity 3.1) during the late Cenozoic. It occurs today in orogenically thickened crust of the Himalaya and Tibetan Plateau, to form small extensional basins throughout Tibet. There the crust has become so thick through compression that gravity is forcing the thickened mass to collapse laterally (Block 4, Section 7.4). Likewise, once the crust in volcanic arcs becomes overly thick, it also collapses laterally (Block 3).

The interiors of Archean continents were very different from those of today (Section 4.5.2). Between the linear orogenic belts where tectonics has added young continental material, modern continents are topographically monotonous, with thin sedimentary cover above ancient cratons. Archean continental relics reveal thick volcanic and sedimentary greenstone belts, that rest on older gneiss complexes. Innumerable granitic plutons formed by crustal melting intrude both crustal components. These intracrustal greenstone belts suffered extensional and compressional strains, and even show signs of a kind of vertical tectonics (Section 4.5.2). Such features suggest that continental lithosphere was inherently weak during the Archean. Provided heat flow was above about $50\,mW\,m^{-2}$, Archean quartz-rich crust would guarantee that weakness (Section 4.2.3).

The strength of rocks is not only determined by mineralogy and heat flow, but also by strain rate and whether strain is extensional or compressive (Block 1, Section 3).

- Under which conditions are rocks stronger: extension or compression?

- Figure 3.11 in Block 1 shows a dramatic difference between the two conditions. For stresses likely to occur in the lithosphere, the modern two-layer continental lithosphere is likely to undergo complete failure at much lower heat flow in an extensional environment than in one dominated by compression.

The differences in compressive and extensional strength apply to the single-layer Archean continental crust, and it would also be much weaker under both conditions. Given the likelihood of higher heat flow in Archean times, due to greater heat production by less-decayed radioactive isotopes, continental lithosphere that had not been depleted in heat-producing isotopes would have deformed easily in response to both compression and especially extension.

> Question 4.8 From Block 2, can you recall the most likely way in which continental lithosphere experiences extensional stress? Suggest some examples.

The tectonic picture that emerges from considerations of heat flow and lithosphere strength is that Archean continents would have been less stable than those of later times. Compression associated with subduction at their margins, particularly when that involved continental collision, would more easily have thickened the crust. However, once isostasy had elevated the most-thickened parts above a threshold when the lithosphere would fail (probably much lower than triggered lateral collapse of the Tibetan Plateau and the Andes), gravitational extensional stress would have induced lateral collapse of the orogens. Mantle plumes beneath the continents would also have induced wholesale extension of the crust on a larger scale than occurs in the East African Rift (Block 2, Section 4.6.6).

- What is the largest modern example of continental extension, and what is the underlying reason for it?

- It is the Basin and Range Province in the western USA (Block 1, Activity 3.1), where the East Pacific Rise has been subducted beneath the westward-moving North American Plate.

The more rapid generation of oceanic lithosphere in the Archean would undoubtedly have resulted in more common subduction of active spreading centres and Basin and Range scenarios. However, the high-magnesium volcanic rocks found in greenstone belts suggest that mantle plumes helped induce continental extension in the Archean.

4.6.1   The end of the beginning

Despite the evidence for the odd behaviour of continental lithosphere during the Archean, you will have concluded from Section 4 that the same large-scale processes of sea-floor spreading and subduction, and the rise of mantle plumes, occurred then as today. The differences lie in the composition of Archean continental crust, because it formed by slab melting, and the probably much larger influence of plumes. One major question is: 'Did Archean conditions slowly evolve to those that characterize the present, or was there a sudden transformation?'.

The very clear geochemical differences between pre- and post-Archean continental crust suggest that the change was brusque, but do not explain the sudden shift. Figure 4.22 shows that after the Archean, the amount of radiogenic ^{87}Sr in the oceans rose from low, constant values before 2500 Ma. Only rocks with plenty of rubidium in them (^{87}Sr forms by decay of ^{87}Rb) are able to add enough radiogenic strontium to the oceans when they are eroded. Relative to the mantle, and basalts derived from it, only felsic igneous rocks have elevated Rb/Sr ratios.

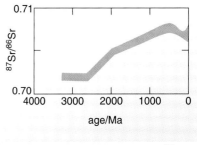

Figure 4.22   The change in the $^{87}Sr/$ ^{86}Sr ratio of seawater through recorded geological time, derived from the isotopic composition of carbonate sediments.

- How, then, might ^{87}Sr have been added to seawater following the Archean?

- The simplest explanations involve either an increase in the amount of continental crust exposed to erosion, or an increase in the rate of continental erosion.

Radiometric dating shows a peak in the number of ages between 3000 and 2500 Ma. Many geologists have interpreted this peak to signify a remarkable pulse in crust generation at the end of the Archean — a crustal 'pandemonium' to quote one enthusiast (Block 3, Figure 7.9, curves 4 and 5). Except for a few milligrams of zircon crystals in later Archean sediments, which do breach the 4000 Ma 'barrier', there is no evidence for pre-4000 Ma continental material (Block 3, Figure 7.9, curves 1 to 3). The late Archean also shows an increase in crustal melting to form sizeable amounts of granite for the first time in Earth's history. Deep-crustal metamorphism that generated granulites similar to those of the Badcallian part of the Lewisian also peaked at the end of the Archean.

As you saw in Section 4.2, heat-producing isotopes are transferred to higher crustal levels by deep-crustal metamorphism. Their depletion in the lower crust, accompanied by erosion of the upper crust, drives down continental heat flow. That in turn creates cratons, whose new-found strength is able to support higher elevations and greater erosion of the upper crust. Most Archean continental nuclei behaved as cratons after 2500 Ma, and everywhere lie beneath profound unconformities (Figure 2.1a). The oldest such craton lies at the heart of southern Africa, which is unconformably overlain by 3000-Ma-old sediments very similar to the Torridonian. Therefore, one contributing factor to the profound shift in continental behaviour after 2500 Ma must have been 'maturing' of the crust.

That still leaves unresolved the end-Archean shift from slab melting to wedge melting. As you found in Question 4.6, most oceanic crust failed to be transformed from hydrous basalt to anhydrous eclogite during the Archean. Modern plate movements depend on the steep descent of dense subducted lithosphere to impart slab-pull force. It also mechanically decouples oceanic lithosphere from that of the continents. Low-angled subduction in the Archean would have enabled plate forces to affect the under-ridden continents, producing more widespread deformation than at post-Archean active continental margins. Heat and water driven upwards from dehydration of modern subducted ocean lithosphere induces the mantle wedge to partially melt. Retention of water in subducted oceanic crust during the Archean would have encouraged partial melting in the slab, probably of garnet amphibolite.

Though still unresolved, a sudden shift to widespread eclogite formation around 2500 Ma would explain a great deal. Despite the greater overall heat production in Archean times, the proportion from the mantle would have been driven down by rapid formation of continental crust. At some time, a threshold level would have been passed that slowed sea-floor spreading sufficiently for subduction of ocean floor that was old enough and cold enough to undergo the basalt-to-eclogite transition. Lots of evidence suggests that this was achieved 2500 Ma ago.

4.6.2 Summary of Section 4.6

- Many features of the Archean suggest that higher heat production before 2500 Ma induced large-scale processes that, while not signifying the non-existence of plate tectonics, took on very different forms from those of later times. In particular, continental lithosphere would have been weaker and more prone to failure in both compressive and extensional regimes. It could have taken up shortening by ductile deformation over wide areas as opposed to the narrow, long orogens of the post-Archean. Extensional collapse would also have been likely, producing widespread basins over thinning crust, akin to the Basin and Range Province of Cenozoic to Recent North America.

- The Paleoproterozoic change from peculiar Archean processes and their products, to those much the same as today, seems to have been sudden. More radiogenic strontium was added to seawater after 2500 Ma, probably because the first cratons stabilized at the end of the Archean, and increased continental erosion transferred large amounts of heat-producing elements to marine sediments. The resulting decrease in continental heat flow would have imparted greater strength to continental lithosphere, so that rugged relief could develop for the first time and thereby increase rates of erosion.

Objectives for Section 4

Now that you have completed this Section, you should be able to:

4.1   Understand the meaning of all the terms printed in **bold**.

4.2   Account for the regional structural and metamorphic features of the Lewisian Complex.

4.3   Apply geochemical, tectonic and thermal concepts that you learned in earlier Blocks to information about Archean complexes.

Question 4.9 What is the evidence for: (a) the role of garnet in the formation of magmas that added to the continents before 2500 Ma ago; (b) the insignificance of feldspar fractionation in the evolution of Archean felsic magmas; (c) the probability that the main sources of volcanism in greenstone belts were mantle plumes? (d) What is the importance of your answer to (b)?

Question 4.10 (a) Why is the Lewisian Complex regarded as a composite of several small fragments of continental crust? (b) What is the main evidence that supports collision of two of these fragments at a destructive margin?

5 Uniting the British Isles

The last deformation and metamorphism that affected the Lewisian Complex, the earliest crustal materials in the British Isles, was at about 1750 Ma in the Paleoproterozoic Era.

> **Question 5.1** On the Tectonic Map, rocks of Paleoproterozoic age (1600 to 2500 Ma) are marked as PP_{1-3} in the key. Three of the units are components of the Lewisian Complex of the NW Highlands and Hebrides. The fourth (pink PP_3) outcrops in small areas from Islay to Clew Bay in western Ireland. Which other Precambrian rocks occur in those localities and what kind of contacts are involved?

The Tectonic Map's key refers to PP_3 as 'Ketilidian', an orogeny that affected the Greenland part of Laurentia at about the same time as the Laxfordian event. Figure 5.1 shows the inferred links between Precambrian orogenic belts in northern Laurentia and Baltica, when they were linked after the Grenville Orogeny at about 1100 Ma.

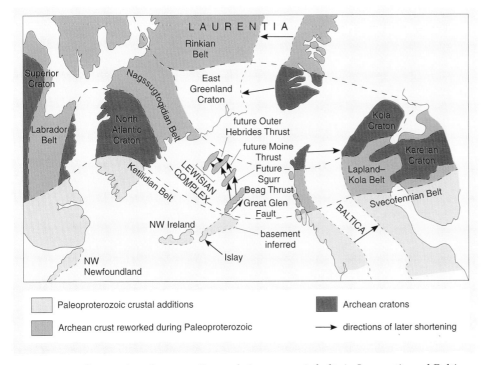

Figure 5.1 Connections between Precambrian orogenic belts in Laurentia and Baltica around 1100 Ma. The gaps connected by arrows in Baltica, and between blocks that eventually became the northern British Isles, indicate the crustal shortening and some strike–slip movements that occurred during Caledonian events.

The video *The Lewisian of NW Scotland* in Activity 4.1 begins with the most spectacular unconformity in Europe (Figure 2.1), which places a virtually unaltered sequence of terrestrial sediments on ancient, deeply eroded Lewisian crust. The unconformity represents an immense time gap, between 500 and 800 Ma long; at least as long as the entire Phanerozoic Eon. During that time, the Rodinia supercontinent came into being (Section 3.2). Though the northern part of the modern British Isles participated in those events, their effects remain almost totally hidden. The southern component had not yet come into being. Our 'local' geology says very little about that part of Earth's evolution, but ideas about global tectonic evolution from about 900 to 400 Ma ago received a major input from the British Isles.

5.1   Neoproterozoic events and terranes

The Neoproterozoic Era (1000 to 545 Ma) immediately preceded the first appearance of fossilized animals' hard parts at the beginning of the Cambrian Period. Although the Precambrian–Phanerozoic boundary has little if any tectonic meaning, it represents an explosive biological change. During the Neoproterozoic, new lithosphere added to the northern and southern parts of the British Isles. The geological history of the southern part probably began in Neoproterozoic times, insofar as geologists have found no signs of rocks older than Neoproterozoic there.

5.1.1   Northern terranes

Northern Scotland's Lewisian infrastructure has affinities with similar rocks in both Laurentia and Baltica (eastern Greenland and modern Scandinavia) welded together before Rodinia formed. Figure 5.2 shows several tiny slivers that formed northern Scotland in relation to the formation of the Grenvillian orogen.

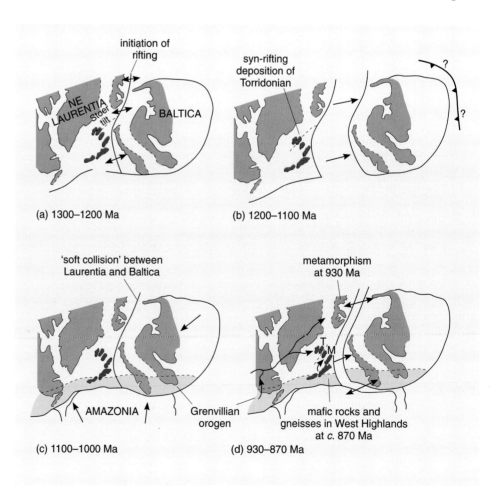

Figure 5.2   Shifting positions of Baltica and Laurentia around the time of the Grenville Orogeny that helped weld together Rodinia about 1100 Ma ago. The pink area in (c) and (d) is the Grenville orogen, formed here through the collision of Amazonia with the other two continental segments. Through this period, Laurentia and Baltica experienced repeated rifting and rift closure, that affected their respective sedimentary records as well as their paleomagnetic positions. Parts that assembled to form the northern British Isles are in red. T = Torridonian; M = Moine.

The horizontal sediments sitting unconformably on Lewisian gneisses in Figure 2.1a are part of a thick sequence of terrestrial sediments, divided into three Groups that are collectively known as the **Torridonian.** Their estimated 12 km thickness is the sum of successive Torridonian Groups measured in different parts of NW Scotland — the full sequence is not preserved in one place. The upper part of the Torridonian formed in a vast system of braided rivers draining the north-eastern part of Laurentia (Figure 5.3). The lowest Group is mainly fluvial in origin with aeolian and lake sediments, but displays transport directions to east and west. Dating terrestrial sedimentary rocks is difficult, but the lowest and uppermost Torridonian Groups have provided imprecise dates of 1200 and 977 Ma respectively. Torridonian strata probably represent sedimentation into a series of rifts that evolved during the jostling of Laurentia and Baltica between 1200 to 1000 Ma, during the formation of Rodinia. The uppermost Torridonian contains transported zircon grains with U–Pb ages as young as 1100 Ma, which suggests that some of the sediment came from the Grenville orogen (Figure 5.2d) in Laurentia. However, the bulk of quartz and feldspar grains, and larger clasts of gneisses, are of Archean and Paleoproterozoic provenance, and were eroded from Greenland and local Lewisian sources.

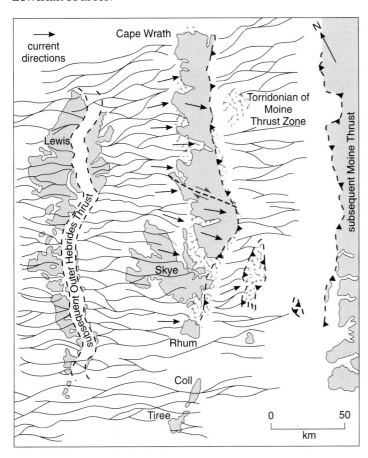

Figure 5.3   Model for the deposition of the Torridonian sandstones by braided rivers flowing from Laurentia, based on paleocurrent data. Broad areas where the Torridonian remains show as bold stipple. Black arrows show current directions. (*Note:* Positions of the Torridonian sandstones are as they were before the Caledonian Orogeny.)

Torridonian rocks do not occur to the east of the Moine Thrust. Movement on the Moine Thrust during the late stages of the Caledonian Orogeny amounted to at least 50 km towards the present north-west. That is a large displacement in British terms, but in a regional context it is minuscule. Some topographic feature of the time must have prevented Torridonian sediments crossing the gap corresponding to Moine Thrust displacement on Figure 5.1. Rocks in the hanging-wall of the Moine Thrust are metamorphosed, shallow-marine sediments, mainly mudstones and sandstones, of the **Moine Supergroup.** They are thought to have a total thickness of around 12 km, in a pair of half-grabens (Block 4, Section 3.2.1). Figure 5.2d suggests that the extension to form the Moine depositional basin coincided with minor rifting of this part of Rodinia. Occurrences in the Moine Supergroup of metamorphosed basaltic igneous rocks suggest that the extension resulted in decompression melting of rising asthenosphere. Figure 5.4 shows large extensional faults that probably controlled the two depositional centres, and suggests how they may have become inverted during later crustal shortening that formed major thrusts. This later, compressional deformation was extreme, so that the Moine rocks define huge isoclinal folds or nappes. Examining the Tectonic Map for this part of northern Scotland shows the cores of these nappes as several thin areas of rocks labelled A–PP$_3$ (Archean and Paleoproterozoic), the crystalline basement on which marine deposition took place. These tectonic inliers resemble the Lewisian Complex, but they are so deformed that it is difficult to prove a connection conclusively.

Figure 5.4   Possible cross-section of the half-grabens in which Moinian marine sediments accumulated. In this interpretation, the major extensional faults became sites for later thrusting that expelled the basin contents north-westwards onto the Hebridean Terrane (see Tectonic Map).

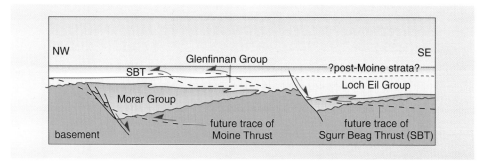

Dating sedimentation of the Moine Supergroup relies entirely on defining a maximum age from dates of detrital minerals, and a minimum age from dates of the oldest igneous bodies that intrude the Moine. Detrital zircons range from 1900 to 1000 Ma, and do not match the age pattern of the Lewisian. Instead they suggest that the sediments which make up the Moine poured into the area from the Grenville orogen. Unlike the transport direction in the Torridonian (Figure 5.3), sedimentary structures in the Moine formed while currents flowed from the south-west; appropriate for their provenance in the Grenville orogen (Figure 5.2d). The earliest igneous intrusions (now granitic gneisses and metagabbros) are 870 Ma old, providing the minimum age of Moine sedimentation. These intrusions pre-date deformation, and may reflect an episode of crustal extension and associated partial melting of crust and rising asthenosphere. High-grade metamorphism and intense deformation affected the Moine Supergroup and the intrusions around 800 Ma. So a rough age for this sedimentary sequence is between 1000 and 870 Ma; the Torridonian and Moine could have formed at the same time. However, the lack of any match other than a tenuous common age, suggests that the line of the much later Moine Thrust is perhaps the accretionary boundary of an exotic block on which the Moine Supergroup accumulated, hence the distinction between the Hebridean and Northern Highland Terranes on the Tectonic Map.

Figure 5.1 indicates the position and likely displacement on the Great Glen Fault, the British Isles' most spectacular strike–slip system. It now separates the Moine Supergroup to its north-west from the **Dalradian Supergroup**, which dominates the Central and Western Highlands (Block 4, Figure 3.4). In Block 4 (Sections 3.1 and 3.2), you looked briefly at some of the evidence for the structural complexity of the Dalradian.

●   What was the supposed connection between the depositional environment of the Dalradian Supergroup and its later tectonic evolution?

● A series of extensional growth faults created several half-grabens in which thicknesses of the sedimentary units changed laterally. Tectonic thickening of the sedimentary pile resulted in inversion of the graben-bounding faults, and some of the later thrusts still preserve the young-on-old relationship between hanging-wall and footwall that would result from their originating as extensional faults.

The lateral differences in thickness of Dalradian sediments in the half-grabens, together with large crustal shortening taken up by the thrusts, resulted in immensely complex major structures (Block 4, Figures 3.7 and 3.8), including huge recumbent folds or nappes. The largest of these structures (the Tay Nappe) expelled sediments to the south-east, so that large areas of the south-east Highlands are now upside down, the upper limb of this nappe having been removed by later erosion. Superficially, the structure of the Dalradian resembles that of the Moine, although compressional vergence is dominantly south-eastwards in the former and north-westwards in the latter. Both were deformed by the Grampian phase of the Caledonian events (Section 5.2). However, the Dalradian Supergroup is the younger sedimentary sequence.

At the base of the Dalradian complex, south-east of Inverness, are a series of migmatites, known as the Central Highland migmatites, that underwent high-grade metamorphism at 800 Ma as did the Moine Supergroup. Like the Moine sediments, the Central Highland migmatites contain zircons with Grenvillian ages, so the sediments from which they formed must have been deposited some time between 1100 and 800 Ma. There are other crystalline rocks spatially associated with the Dalradian, but as tectonically isolated occurrences in Islay, on Inishtrahull island north of Ulster, and in western Ireland (marked PP_3 on the Tectonic Map). They give ages of igneous and metamorphic crystallization around 1710 to 1780 Ma. Apart from these occurrences, there is no surface evidence for a crystalline basement to the Dalradian. This evidence suggests that Dalradian sedimentation formed on different crust from that beneath the Moine. The Dalradian may have formed in a different terrane from that of the Moine Supergroup — the Grampian as opposed to the Northern Highland Terrane (inset to Tectonic Map).

Dalradian sedimentation must have begun after 800 Ma. The supergroup contains three possible time markers (Figure 5.5). The youngest comprises Middle Cambrian (509 Ma) limestones and shales. A series of metamorphosed basalt lavas occur lower in the succession of the south-west Highlands (the Tayvallich lavas). They probably formed in a small extensional basin around 600 Ma. The middle of the sequence includes the distinctive Port Askaig Tillite, deposited by floating ice-shelves; distinctive not only because of its glacial origin but because the area was at low latitudes during glaciation. This is a product of one of the celebrated Neoproterozoic 'Snowball Earth' events. Unfortunately, there seem to have been several such 'Snowball' events between 970 and 570 Ma, and the Port Askaig Tillite could just as well be correlated with several of those that pre-date the Tayvallich volcanics. One view is that the tillites correlate with a global glaciation around 720 Ma. So, the time-span that Dalradian sedimentation represents is uncertain, but is of the order of 300 Ma, comparable with the whole of Mesozoic time.

Unsurprisingly, such a lengthy period of Dalradian deposition covers many changes in depositional environment, summarized by Figure 5.5:

1   variable and episodic subsidence related to a series of fault-bounded basins;

2   sagging of the basin floors as thermal anomalies related to crustal thinning waned so that overall density of the crust increased slightly;

3   fluctuations in sediment supply and rates of filling of the basins;

4   global changes in sea-level, some in response to repeated glacial conditions that dwarfed those of the present Ice Age.

You will see that almost every conceivable kind of sedimentary environment, except for terrestrial varieties, is present in the Dalradian Supergroup. Note that coarse clastic sediments in the lower part of the Dalradian are quartz sands, signifying debris from evolved crust that was sorted over protracted periods. Those in the upper parts are turbidites, and contain large amounts of fresh feldspar. Its presence suggests that by the middle of the Argyll Group the source of debris had been stripped down to crystalline basement, whatever that was. Sedimentary structures show transport of debris towards the present south-east, so the source lay to the north-west, possibly in the older, metamorphosed and granite-permeated Northern Highland Terrane.

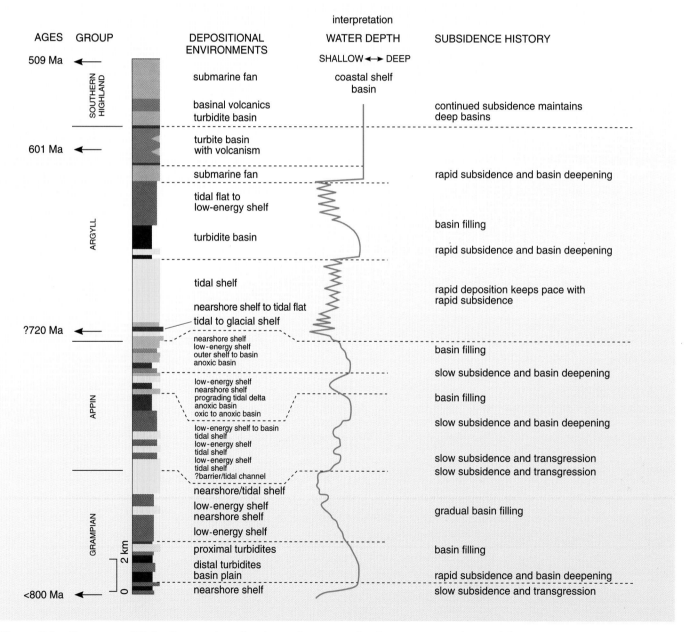

Figure 5.5   Summary of Dalradian stratigraphy, the environments that it represents and two of the important controls (water depth and subsidence history). Whereas the relative thicknesses are approximately accurate, it is unlikely that any area experienced sedimentation throughout Dalradian times. Basins of sedimentation probably moved with time, as extension of the crust progressed.

Contemporary events were very different in the Outer Zone of the Caledonides. North-west of the Moine Thrust Zone, a mere 1.5 km of Cambrian to Early Ordovician sediments (dark blue EP_{1-2} on the Tectonic Map) that formed in a stable shelf environment rest unconformably on the Torridonian. The lowermost of these shelf sediments are Early Cambrian, but deposition continued there until about 470 Ma, whereas the youngest Dalradian is 509 Ma. Erosion had reduced the Hebridean Terrane to a planar surface over a period of about 450 Ma, and the Cambro-Ordovician cover represents a major marine transgression, recognizable on many continents. This probably resulted from increased sea-floor spreading that broke up the Neoproterozoic supercontinents during the Early Cambrian (Figure 3.7a), and reduced the volume of the ocean basins.

It is possible to visualize how conditions changed during the development of the Dalradian basins by comparing Figures 3.4 and 3.6.

⬤ What happened to the paleolatitude of the northern British Isles through the Neoproterozoic?

⬤ It changed from equatorial to being close to the South Pole.

Whatever the global climate, weathering would have changed from dominantly chemical to physical, and this shift helps explain the absence of limestones from the upper Dalradian (Figure 5.5).

⬤ What major tectonic feature would have dominated Dalradian deposition?

⬤ Figure 3.6, for around 580 Ma ago, shows rifting of South America from Laurentia, close to the position of the northern British Isles. The extensional basins in which Dalradian sediments accumulated are best explained as results of this regional crustal thinning.

The acceleration in subsidence around the end of deposition of the Appin Group, after slow subsidence in earlier Dalradian basins, possibly signifies the initiation of this continental break-up. Whatever, the northern part of the British Isles suddenly found itself on the flank of a growing ocean, which you will recall is named Iapetus.

Figure 5.5 gives the impression that the Dalradian represents a very long period of continuous sedimentation, unbroken by any tectonic events — it shows no unconformities. Until recently, most geologists were content with such a view, for no-one had discovered evidence for breaks in sedimentation that unconformities signify. That is unsurprising because of the structural complexity (Block 4), which resulted from later events that involved polyphase, ductile deformation. However, there are several features that have long puzzled Dalradian specialists.

Question 5.2 Using the scale on Figure 5.5, estimate the total thickness of the Dalradian. What does this imply for the lowermost Groups during deposition of the youngest ones?

The total thickness of exposed Dalradian sediments is far greater than found in any younger sedimentary basins, and what is more, no period around 300 Ma long is known anywhere else to have involved unbroken sedimentation. Geologists established the Dalradian sequence from local evidence of what lies upon what. In fact, there is no evidence that all the Groups occur in one place. There may have been lateral variations in the thickness of each, the focus of deposition may have shifted with time, so that the Groups may have accumulated in different places, and finer-grained rocks, now slates, almost certainly were tectonically thickened.

Between 3 to 4°W and 56° 40′ to 57° N on the Tectonic Map, you will find a small occurrence marked in red with black dots, and labelled NP₃. In the legend, this signifies a syntectonic 'Older Granite' intrusion. The Ben Vuirich granite is 590 ± 2 Ma old, intrudes the Argyll Group and has high initial $^{87}Sr/^{86}Sr$ ratios (Block 3, Box 4.5), showing that it formed by crustal melting. One interpretation is that the Ben Vuirich granite and its aureole represents an orogenic episode involving considerable crustal thickening shortly after the eruption of the Tayvallich lavas. Another is that magmas supplying both the Ben Vuirich granite and the Tayvallich lavas formed as a result of major crustal extension. Either process would have interrupted Dalradian sedimentation, perhaps shifting the focus for deposition of the Southern Highland Group. You touched on the Grampian Terrane's structural complexity in Block 4, and will meet it again shortly.

5.1.2   Southern terranes

Compared with the northern British Isles, occurrences of Neoproterozoic rocks in southern parts are few and far between. On the Tectonic Map they show as pale grey tones labelled NP₂ and NP₃. Spend a few moments seeking out a few such occurrences.

You should have spotted moderate-sized areas near Rosslare in County Waterford, on the Lleyn Peninsula, Anglesey, and around the Longmynd in Shropshire. You need a sharp eye to see the lettering in the Malverns, Nuneaton (north-east of Coventry) and Charnwood Forest (south-west of Leicester), where Neoproterozoic occurrences are too small to show. Figure 5.6 shows all the occurrences in England and Wales, including a couple from boreholes in the East Midlands. Ages range from 677 to 560 Ma, within the time-span of Dalradian deposition. There all resemblance ends, which is hardly surprising because these rocks evolved far from the northern British Isles (Figure 3.6). There are intriguing examples of high-grade gneisses, in Rosslare and Anglesey, the Malverns and in Shropshire. Analysis of neodymium isotopes in deformed calc-alkaline plutonic rocks, which are associated with gneisses in the Malverns, suggests that the magmas from which they formed at 677 Ma incorporated older crustal rocks. The isotope data suggest that this older, unexposed crust formed from mantle-derived arc magmas between 1000 and 1200 Ma. This is the only

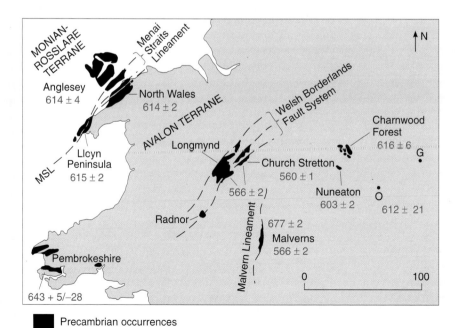

Figure 5.6   Occurrences of Neoproterozoic rocks in England and Wales, including radiometric ages (in Ma) of extrusive and intrusive igneous rocks. O and G are boreholes that reach basement in the East Midlands. MSL = Menai Straits Lineament.

indication of a possible basement for Avalonia, and the age range suggests that it formed during the assembly of Rodinia, probably in connection with the collision of Amazonia, Baltica and Laurentia (Figure 3.4).

Aside from the rocks of the Longmynd in Shropshire, which are a series of sediments that record fluctuations between terrestrial and marine conditions, the remaining occurrences east of the Menai Straits have igneous components. These include lavas of basaltic, andesitic and felsic composition, with ashes formed on land or in shallow water.

● What kind of tectonic environment might volcanic rocks with such a compositional range signify?

● They are typical of a volcanic arc above a subduction zone.

Figure 5.6 shows that large faults juxtapose different groups of these rocks. It is quite possible that the components of the Midland Craton (Section 2.1) could represent several small terranes. However, evidence is scanty, and they are generally referred to as Avalonian (Section 3.2.3), part of the Avalonia Terrane (Figure 3.7e). Together with Armorica, they represent a large and long-lived subduction-zone environment situated at the northern edge of Gondwana (the Cadomian volcanic arc on Figure 3.6).

Activity 5.1

This Activity is based on the video *The Geology of Anglesey*, and should take you about 90 minutes.

The Neoproterozoic of Anglesey and Lleyn, together with Rosslare, is different. A line roughly along that of the Menai Straits separates it from the Precambrian of the rest of the southern British Isles. The oldest rocks are an astonishingly diverse mixture in such a tiny area. The association of oceanic basalts, a mélange and blueschists, plus possible mantle rocks, suggest that at least part of the complexity relates directly to subduction and complex development of an accretionary prism. Yet these rocks are now closely related to metasediments that contain so much quartz that they must have been derived from evolved crust, either an older continental mass or an arc volcanic complex. In the same small area, metamorphic grade ranges from greenschist facies to upper amphibolite and blueschist facies. The small blocks could not have formed close to one another, and their sharp contacts, probably shear zones, suggest that these are tiny terranes that accreted by strike–slip tectonics.

5.1.3 Summary of Section 5.1

• The Neoproterozoic of the northern British Isles has three main components — the Torridonian, Moine and Dalradian Supergroups — dated between 1200 and 977 Ma, 1000–870 Ma, and 800–509 Ma respectively. All three are mainly sedimentary in origin. Of the three, only the Torridonian is unmetamorphosed. They formed in extensional basins produced at different times at the margin of Laurentia, during several phases of Neoproterozoic rifting. Differences in the source of their sediments, together with their different tectonic histories, suggest that each rests on what were different terranes — the Hebridean, Northern Highland and Grampian Terranes respectively.

- The earliest widespread metamorphism of the Moine took place 800 Ma ago, and seemed also to have affected the Central Highland migmatites, beneath the Dalradian metasediments. Moine metasediments are tectonically sliced together with older gneisses, that appear to be similar, if not identical to those of the Lewisian Complex. An Archean basement seems likely for the Northern Highland Terrane, whereas that for the Grampian Terrane is at most Paleoproterozoic.

- The great apparent thickness of the Dalradian implies that its sedimentary evolution is a great deal more problematic than geologists have assumed. Such a thickness beneath one place could not have escaped high-grade metamorphism and crustal melting in its lower parts. It is unlikely that the 300 Ma of Dalradian deposition could have been tectonically uninterrupted. Shifts in the centres of sedimentation may resolve this paradox. The Caledonian structural complexity of the Dalradian might rule out finding evidence for earlier tectonic events during its evolution.

- The Neoproterozoic of the southern British Isles is very different from that of the north, since it evolved far off on a different continental margin. Most of it is hidden by Phanerozoic rocks. It evolved from 677 to 560 Ma ago, but apart from some tiny exposures of gneissic rocks, there is little sign of the basement on which it formed. There are two distinct terranes, one to the east of a line roughly along the Menai Straits that has dominant arc volcanics, and the other on the Lleyn Peninsula, Anglesey and in Rosslare. The terranes formed in a destructive margin environment, as opposed to the extensional margins that dominated evolution of the northern terranes.

5.2 Orogenies and terrane accretion during the Lower Paleozoic

Paleomagnetic pole data and inferences from local geology show that, in the first 100 Ma of the Lower Paleozoic, what was to become the southern British Isles parted company with Gondwana. Its drift towards the opposite margin of the Iapetus Ocean ended around Middle Silurian times (420 Ma), with the amalgamation of the British Isles' lithosphere, largely as we know it. Accomplishing this demanded the subduction of all oceanic lithosphere beneath Iapetus and long-distance movement of several crustal fragments to accrete as several terranes (inset to Tectonic Map). Until that welding, the principal components continued to evolve as separate entities.

The appearance of abundant shelly organisms at the start of the Cambrian provided means of dividing time and correlating sedimentary rocks that formed in different places. By connecting far-separated rocks and the environments that they represent, stratigraphers are more easily able to deduce a relative sequence of global events, aided by radiometric dating of extrusive igneous rocks and some sediments.

- By examining Figure 3.7, can you suggest any problems with faunal correlation between the components that eventually accreted to form the British Isles?

- Through the Early Cambrian until the Silurian, different continental masses, and the terranes that make up the British Isles, shifted geographic position. Not only might separation by large oceans have affected the animal species that evolved in different parts of the Lower Paleozoic world, but there would undoubtedly have been adaptations to different climatic conditions. Southern parts of the British Isles lay at high southern latitudes until well into the Ordovician, while the northern components were tropical, or nearly so, throughout the Era.

Figure 3.7b shows that there were indeed significant differences between the fossil records of the northern and southern British Isles through the Lower Paleozoic. The four faunal provinces mainly reflect differences among trilobites, unlikely to have scuttled back and forth across oceans. These faunal differences prevent precise correlation of Lower Paleozoic events between the northern and southern components of the British Isles. Yet paleontological change in each component helps put the sequence of tectonic events and environments that affected each in precise order. Another advantage is that, while different faunal communities continued to characterize each component, geologists can be reasonably sure that those parts were sufficiently isolated from each other for there to be neither mingling nor competition to create a unified fossil record. The first hint that the Iapetus Ocean once existed came not from paleomagnetic data or evidence of crustal evolution, but from the profound faunal differences in Cambrian and Ordovician sediments between northern and southern parts of the British Isles. They support the notion of entirely separate geological evolution in the areas in which they are found, and that, as you will see, characterized northern and southern parts for much of the Lower Paleozoic.

One group of organisms does permit continent-to-continent correlation between Lower Paleozoic rocks. They were colonial, planktonic animals, known as graptolites, that could mix across oceans because of surface currents. Even they were not truly global, for like all plankton, climate probably played a role in the geographic range of individual species. The graptolites failed to survive beyond the end of the Silurian, but they served their purpose by finely 'calibrating' Lower Paleozoic stratigraphy.

5.2.1   Events in the North

Around 509 Ma ago, Dalradian sedimentation came to a halt. Thereafter, the Dalradian Supergroup began to deform, culminating in a series of vast nappes, as once again did the Moine Supergroup. The outcome is shown by a complex cross-section from the Highland Boundary Fault to the Moine Thrust Zone (Figure 5.7).

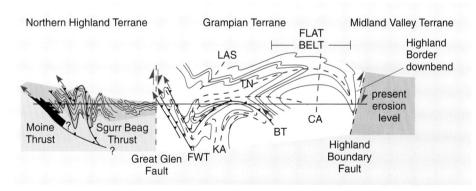

Figure 5.7   Simplified structural cross-section from NW to SE across the North Highland and Grampian Terranes of Scotland. FWT Fort William Thrust; BT Iltay Bounday Thrust/Slide (Block 4 pp. 39–41); KA Kinlochleven Anticline; TN Tay Nappe; LAS Loch Awe Synform; CA Cowal Antiform.

The principles of fold interference (Block 4, Section 5.1.3) suggest that three major episodes of folding affected the Dalradian. Figure 5.7 and the Tectonic Map show this through the bending of axial planes of the major structures. The nappes that dominate the south-east Highlands have root zones that fold earlier, large-scale structures in the Fort William area (next to the Great Glen Fault). The nappes, in turn, are folded by a huge upright open fold in the south-east.

As in the case of the Himalaya (Block 4, Section 7.5.2), crustal thickening in the Grampian Terrane induced a major change in the geotherm, and regional metamorphism evolved to high-grade conditions. Figure 6.21 in Block 4 shows the distribution of the highest-grade metamorphic mineral zones that affect the Dalradian, which reached sillimanite-zone conditions that induced partial melting over large tracts in the north-east of the Grampian Terrane. In the south-west, the metamorphic zones are themselves folded. However, analysing the textural relationships between mineral growth and minor structures related to the major folds (Block 4, Section 6.2.1, and Activity 6.2) reveals that the climax of metamorphism was later than the two largest sets of structures in Figure 5.7. Metamorphic garnets have radiometric ages of 473 ± 3 Ma in garnet-grade rocks, and 465 ± 3 Ma in those at sillimanite grade. As luck would have it, layered mafic–ultramafic intrusions in the NE of the Grampian Terrane (purple EP_2 on the Tectonic Map), themselves affected by later folding, cut across the main mineral zones and superimpose their own thermal effects in the form of renewed growth of sillimanite. These 'Younger Gabbros' give Middle Ordovician ages of 470 ± 9 Ma. The mafic–ultramafic complex is a product of mantle melting beneath tectonically thickened crust, perhaps in response to convective removal of thickened lithosphere.

Thickening of the Grampian Terrane crust spanned at least 25 Ma, beginning some time in the Early Ordovician, reaching its climax at around 470 Ma and continuing as later folding episodes, such as the Cowal Antiform (Figure 5.7). Erosion of the undoubtedly elevated surface probably complicated thermal evolution (Block 4, Figure 7.9). By analogy with the Himalaya, it seems likely that this **Grampian phase** of the Caledonian orogeny was a response to some kind of collision, following subduction at what had been a long-lived extensional margin to the Iapetus Ocean. You can see evidence for this in the form of ophiolites intimately associated with deformed Dalradian rocks on the Tectonic Map, where they are marked in dark green, together with a code indicating their age.

● Where are there ophiolites of EP_2 age (Early Ordovician) on the Tectonic Map? Are all associated directly with Dalradian rocks? (*Note:* the inset shows ophiolites of different ages, so use this as a guide to their relationships on the Tectonic Map.)

● Large Early Ordovician ophiolites occur in the Shetlands, near the Southern Uplands Fault in SW Scotland (Ballantrae) and in Tyrone (Northern Ireland). Smaller occurrences are dotted along the Highland Boundary Fault, and on the coast of Clew Bay in western Ireland, where the Highland Boundary Fault continues, albeit split into several faults. The Ballantrae ophiolite sits far from Dalradian rocks. Only the Shetland ophiolite truly has a direct association with the Grampian Terrane (Tectonic Map inset), but the rest form a chain along the Highland Boundary Fault, which separates them from the Dalradian.

A close look at the Shetland ophiolite (dated at 492 Ma — lowermost Ordovician) on the Tectonic Map shows that it is thrust over Dalradian rocks. Those along the Highland Boundary Fault, also in tectonic contact with the Dalradian, are in slivers together with Early Ordovician pillow lavas, deep-water shales and cherts, succeeded by conglomerates and some limestones. One tiny occurrence on Achill Island in western Ireland also includes rocks that contain relics of blueschist-grade (high-pressure, low-temperature) metamorphic minerals (Block 4, Section 6.2.3). Although the evidence is disputed, all these ophiolites and associated rocks contain minor structures, such as cleavage and lineations, that match counterparts in the Dalradian nearby. Tiny as most of the occurrences are, they seem likely to have been obducted onto the Grampian Terrane before or during the Grampian phase, the Irish blueschists confirming the existence of a subduction zone. The ophiolites also seem to have been deformed by the same major structures as the Dalradian Supergroup, yet did not experience regional metamorphism in thickened crust. They probably formed a tectonic cap to the Grampian orogen.

⬤ From the stratigraphic sequence in the Dalradian (Figure 5.5), is there any evidence that such subduction passed beneath the Grampian Terrane, i.e. descending to the present north-west?

⬤ The Dalradian contains no volcanic rocks akin to those of a continental volcanic arc, which you would expect to form by partial melting in the mantle wedge overriding a subduction zone dipping beneath the Grampian Terrane (Block 3).

The only alternative is that the subduction, which eventually resulted in obduction of blueschists and ophiolites, descended in the opposite direction, i.e. to the present-day south-east. More of this later.

As you saw in Section 2.2.2 (Figure 2.13), the Iapetus Suture descends north-westwards from a line roughly linking Northumberland through the Solway Firth to just north of Dublin and beyond (inset to Tectonic Map). There can be little doubt that the Iapetus Suture and the subduction zone inferred from the Ordovician ophiolites were not one and the same.

The Midland Valley of Scotland, the Southern Uplands and their equivalents in Ireland expose plenty of Lower Paleozoic rocks, but none older than Early Ordovician (about 485 Ma). Although folded and faulted together, they do not show the intense deformation and high-grade metamorphism that characterizes the Dalradian Supergroup to the north of the Highland Boundary Fault. Upper Paleozoic rocks that occupy much of the Midland Valley obscure virtually everything that lies beneath them. The gravity and seismic refraction data that you studied in Sections 2.1 and 2.2 show that the crust beneath the Midland Valley is quite different from that below the Grampian Terrane. Although the thickest in the British Isles, it creates a positive gravity anomaly, in contrast to the large negative anomaly beneath the Highlands, so it must be the denser of the two segments. Seismic studies reveal fundamental differences between crust underneath the Highlands and that beneath southern Scotland, with a sharp contrast at the Highland Boundary Fault. Yet the crust below the Midland Valley and Southern Uplands also reveals two seismically distinct blocks (Figure 2.10) separated by the line of the Southern Uplands Fault. Upper Paleozoic lavas in the Midland Valley (Section 6) contain xenoliths of the deep crust there (Section 6.1), which are granulite-grade felsic and mafic igneous rocks and metasediments, with no sign of a Precambrian basement akin to the Lewisian or Neoproterozoic gneisses. It seems highly likely that the crust between the Highland Boundary Fault and the line of the Iapetus Suture comprises two distinct terranes — the Midland Valley and Southern Uplands Terranes (inset to Tectonic Map). Judging the constituents of the Midland Valley Terrane is only possible from indirect evidence.

The key area lies just to the north of the Southern Uplands Fault, near Girvan and Ballantrae in SW Scotland, where sedimentary rocks of Ordovician age lie on top of the Ballantrae ophiolite (Figure 5.8). The ophiolite contains thin, deep-water shales with an Early Ordovician graptolite fauna. Conditions changed abruptly from quiet oceanic to an influx of vast amounts of debris in the younger Ordovician sediments. They mix conglomerates, fluviatile sands, marine turbidites and occasional limestones, and contain sufficient, rapidly evolving faunas to chart relative time precisely. Sedimentation continued in the Midland Valley and Southern Uplands Terranes into the Silurian, and neither underwent crustal thickening during the Grampian phase to drive up the surface and induce erosion. Plots of grain size against grain composition at different levels in the Ordovician of the southern Midland Valley Terrane (Figure 5.8) reveal indirect evidence for the evolution of the conglomerates' source. They are extremely coarse, with boulders up to half a metre across. That fact alone suggests a large increase in the energy of the environment after

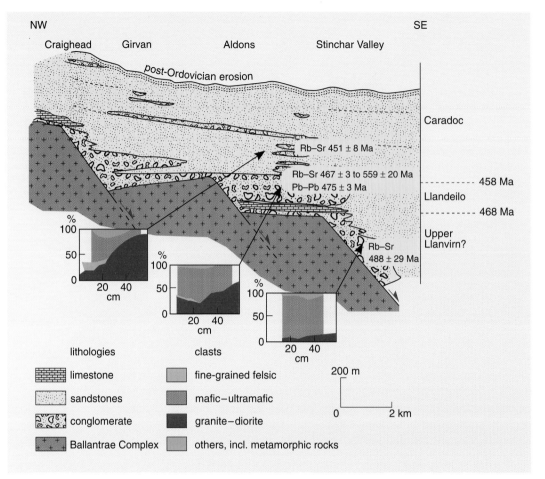

Figure 5.8 Ordovician sedimentary rocks of the Girvan–Ballantrae area, which accumulated in the hanging-walls of several extensional faults that propagated north-westwards with time. The inset graphs plot the percentages of different clasts in the conglomerates against their grain size, at different levels in the sequence.

emplacement of the ophiolite, and such large boulders cannot have moved very far from their source. Current directions are from the north-west, and this source area must have had considerable topographic relief. The most revealing feature of the conglomerates is how the composition of clasts changed with time.

> **Question 5.3** Briefly describe how the composition of clasts in the conglomerates of the Girvan–Ballantrae area (Figure 5.8) changed with time.

Many of the granitic clasts are fresh enough to be dated. Their ages range from about 450 to 560 Ma, i.e. late Neoproterozoic to almost the same age as their enclosing sediments (note that most of these ages are from poor quality Rb–Sr dating; more precise U–Pb dates are all Ordovician). Although there are granitic rocks in the Highlands, the vast majority are much younger (see Section 5.3). Moreover, the granitic clasts are compositionally very similar to those of the modern Andes. These evolved, plutonic igneous rocks are products of magmatic processes in a volcanic arc. A few of the clasts are of metamorphic rocks, so far undated, but they are unlike Dalradian rocks. Together with the high-grade rocks caught up in Upper Paleozoic magmas, such clasts suggest that earlier evolved crust lies beneath the Midland Valley. The evidence in the Girvan–Ballantrae area implies that from the late Neoproterozoic until the Late Ordovician, the Midland Valley was a volcanic arc, i.e. a distinct terrane. In south County Mayo in Ireland there are thick Early Ordovician sediments, derived by rapid erosion of arc volcanoes. They too contain abundant clasts of calc-alkaline igneous rocks and a few thin layers of lavas and pyroclastic rocks. Several arc-type igneous bodies, ranging from gabbros through diorites to granites, intrude the South Mayo sediments, and yield ages of between 470 and 475 Ma.

Figure 5.9 shows one view of the likely tectonics that may have been involved in the development of a volcanic arc in the Midland Valley and south Mayo over a south-east-dipping subduction zone. In Figure 5.9a, off the margin of Laurentia, where the Dalradian Supergroup accumulated in half-grabens from the late Neoproterozoic to Early Ordovician, ocean floor descends beneath what became the Midland Valley Terrane, to give arc volcanism there. Consumption of the marginal ocean floor resulted in collision between this arc complex and Laurentia (Figure 5.9b). That compressed the contents of the Dalradian basins, and expelled any remaining oceanic crust as an obducted nappe of ophiolite over the zone of compressional tectonics.

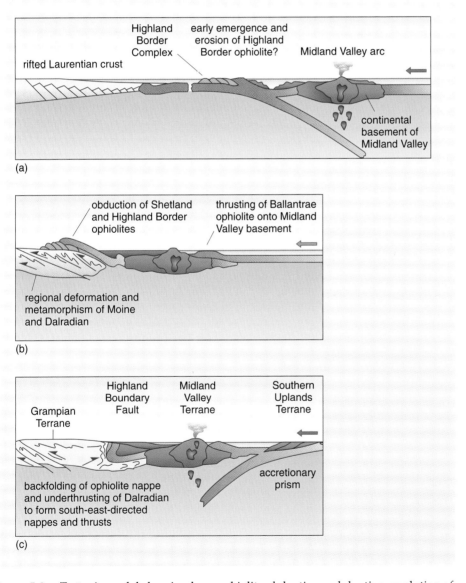

Figure 5.9 Tectonic model showing how ophiolite obduction, subduction, evolution of the Grampian phase and the accretion of the Midland Valley Terrane may be related. (a) The scenario for late Neoproterozoic to Early Ordovician times. (b) Collision of the Midland Valley Terrane with Laurentia and the onset of crustal thickening in the Early Ordovician. (c) 'Flipping' of subduction and how underthrusting of ophiolites associated with the Highland Boundary Fault may have induced south-eastwards expulsion of the major Dalradian nappes. (*Note*: the Midland Valley Terrane probably docked with the Grampian Terrane by left-lateral strike–slip, i.e. it moved 'into' the page.)

So far, this fits with the evidence, including that for the north-westward vergence of the earliest thrusts in the Dalradian and Moine (Figure 5.7). Arc–continent collision would have halted south-eastward subduction. The Ballantrae ophiolite rode up onto the Midland Valley Terrane during the Early Ordovician, at the start of the Grampian phase that profoundly deformed the Dalradian. Yet production of arc magma in the Midland Valley Terrane continued until at least 450 Ma (Figure 5.8), 20 Ma after the formation of the Dalradian nappes and the climax of Grampian metamorphism. The only explanation for that is that subduction restarted beneath the Midland Valley Terrane, but with an opposite sense of motion. Figure 5.9c suggests that the sense of subduction 'flipped' at some time in the Early Ordovician. Flipping of subduction is known from modern times, and an analogy for the Grampian phase is the Neogene evolution of the Banda Arc in Indonesia, where Australian continental crust is in the process of collision with the Timor microcontinent (Figure 5.10).

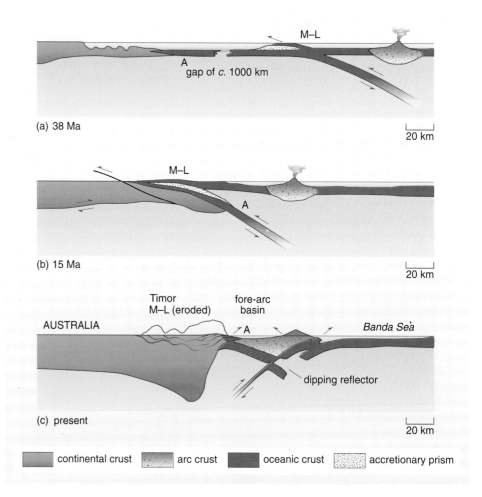

Figure 5.10 Evolution of the Banda Arc since 38 Ma ago, as the Australian lithosphere became involved in the subduction. M–L and A are the Mutis–Lolotoi and Aileu ophiolite complexes.

The ophiolite occurrences that form a chain along the present Highland Boundary Fault are part of a low-grade duplex of fault-bounded slivers (the **Highland Border Complex**). The oldest materials are undated serpentinites (hydrated ultramafic rocks), overlain unconformably by conglomerates and limestones that contain Early Ordovician fossils (about 475 Ma). A tectonically separate assemblage consists of highly altered oceanic pillow lavas with deep-water shales and cherts, which contain fossils that signify an age of about 465 Ma. The youngest rocks are limestones and sandstones with Late Ordovician faunas (aged about 445 Ma).

● Do the ages of rocks in the Highland Border Complex tally with the record from the Dalradian, from which they are now separated by the Highland Boundary Fault?

● No, they do not. Sedimentation in the Highland Border Complex continued for at least 25 Ma after the climax of the Grampian phase.

The Grampian phase climaxed at 470 Ma, so that for an unknown time before and certainly for tens of million years afterwards the Grampian Terrane would have been a mountain belt, subject to intense erosion. Had the Highland Border Complex been emplaced against the Dalradian in its present position at the climax of the Grampian phase, not only would it have experienced that pandemonium of deformation and metamorphism, but sedimentation would have stopped. Figure 5.9c suggests that renewed compression due to northward subduction beneath the Midland Valley Terrane drove the dense ophiolite associated with the Highland Boundary Fault downwards, thereby expelling the Dalradian nappes south-eastwards. You should recognize that not only is this speculative, but it conflicts with the evidence of sedimentation in the Highland Border Complex during and after the climax of Dalradian deformation and metamorphism. Events at the southern margin of the Grampian Terrane are something of a puzzle.

● Can you suggest a mechanism that could have juxtaposed rocks with such very different histories as the Dalradian and the Highland Border Complex?

● Large scale strike–slip motions can slide together once distantly separated blocks.

In western Ireland and the Isle of Arran, where the Highland Boundary Fault also occurs, there is evidence for sinistral strike–slip movement along it in the Early Ordovician. The key to *when* the Highland Border Complex and the Midland Valley Terrane reached approximately their present position relative to the Grampian Terrane again lies in what their Ordovician sediments contain. In both the Girvan and Highland Border Complex sediments, there are no clasts that resemble Dalradian rocks until the Late Ordovician, when metamorphic garnets with nearly identical compositions to those from the high-grade Dalradian occur. The final assembly of the Grampian and Midland Valley Terranes was by lateral motion; the Midland Valley Terrane slid north-eastwards to 'dock' in its present position by the end of the Ordovician. In later times, the Highland Boundary Fault developed to become a huge normal fault (it is still occasionally active), so destroying most of the evidence for Lower Paleozoic evolution in this area.

Ordovician sediments south of the Southern Uplands Fault are very different from those of the Midland Valley Terrane. The area consists of several blocks bounded by large northward-dipping faults. Although each block suffered folding in later times, the sediments in each of them show a general northward sense of stratigraphic younging (Figure 5.11a).

● From the preceding information, deduce what the sense of dip–slip movement on the faults would have been.

● Each places older rocks in the hanging-wall upon younger rocks in the footwall, so they are thrust faults.

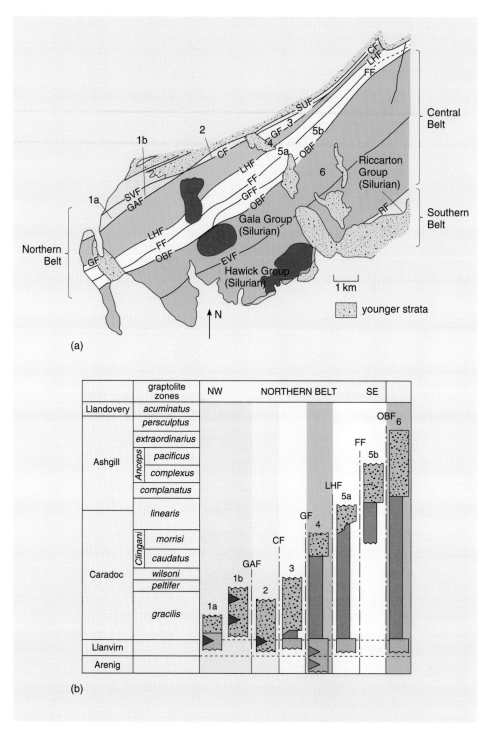

Figure 5.11 Geological features of the Ordovician of the Southern Uplands. (a) Division of Lower Paleozoic rocks into several fault-bounded blocks. Red areas are Silurian to Devonian granites; stippled areas are younger strata. (b) Differences in stratigraphic sequence between the fault blocks in (a). The vertical scale relates to time, i.e. the duration of different sedimentary conditions, rather than to thicknesses. Numbered sections refer to the various blocks in (a). The pale-grey unit at the base of each section represents ocean-floor cherts and mudstones; green is mafic volcanic rocks; dark grey represents mudstones, and orange dotted units are sandy turbidites. Labels ending in 'F' (e.g. SUF) refer to major faults in the Southern Uplands.

There are differences in stratigraphic sequence between the fault blocks in the Southern Uplands (Figure 5.11b). Going south-eastwards, the blocks show increasing duration of mudstone deposition and decreasing age for the start of coarse turbidite sedimentation (Figure 5.11b). Mudstones represent low-energy, probably deep-water sediments deposited far from a source of sedimentary debris. Their duration indicates the length of time that the blocks were far offshore, and that becomes greater towards the south-east. Similarly, the onset of coarse clastic deposition, indicating a nearby, high-relief source of sediment, becomes progressively younger to the south-east. Blocks 1a and 1b, and 2, were close to a clastic source from the time that the ocean floor formed, whereas blocks 3 to 6 approached such an area progressively later in their sedimentary evolution. These features suggest that the blocks formed progressively farther offshore to the south-east. The close association of the blocks today suggests that they were imbricated together by north-dipping thrusts in an accretionary prism (Block 3, Section 5), their age of accretion becoming younger south-eastwards. Because thrusting can form by any kind of compressional tectonics, there are alternative models for the Southern Uplands Terrane: it may have formed as either a back-arc or fore-arc basin to the north of the subduction zone, and was imbricated during the Late Silurian collisional orogeny. The lack of defining evidence (largely because of poor exposure) favours the accretionary prism model, because it is the simplest, albeit imperfect, explanation.

Much of block 6 and two further blocks to the south-east are blanketed by Silurian turbidites, the bulk of which comprises sandstones. This signifies that the Southern Uplands Terrane had completed its accretion to the rest of Scotland by the end of the Ordovician. As in the case of the Midland Valley Terrane and the Highland Border Complex, geologists suspect the influence of strike–slip movements, in this case distributed along the imbricate thrusts, in the final docking of the Southern Uplands Terrane.

5.2.2 Summary of Section 5.2.1

- The recognition of two main components that eventually formed most of the British Isles, separated by a wide Iapetus Ocean, stems from the differences in Lower Paleozoic fossil assemblages between their northern and southern parts.

- From 509 Ma the Dalradian was subjected to the effects of the Grampian phase of the Caledonian Orogeny, and now reveals at least three generations of regional-scale folds. Metamorphism peaked after the first two of these, at around 470 Ma, coinciding with the emplacement of large mafic–ultramafic intrusions (the Younger Gabbros).

- Ophiolites occur close to the Dalradian, the Shetland mass having been thrust over it. The remainder are to the south of the Highland Boundary Fault, in association with various sedimentary rocks. Together with an Irish occurrence of associated blueschists, the ophiolites suggest a subduction zone along the line of the Highland Boundary Fault, from which they were obducted to form a tectonic cap to the Grampian orogen. The lack of any evidence for arc magmatism in the Dalradian rules out subduction beneath the Grampian Terrane, the direction being towards the present south-east.

- The Southern Uplands Fault marks another 'ophiolite-decorated' suture of Lower Paleozoic age, and separates crustal segments with different seismic properties and density, and different sedimentary and volcanic sequences. Neither suffered deformation and metamorphism to the same extent as the Dalradian. Ordovician sediments of the Midland Valley and the south Mayo area of Ireland contain clasts of plutonic, arc-type igneous rocks that range in age from late Neoproterozoic to the age of the enclosing sediments. The most reasonable hypothesis for their origin is a now-hidden magmatic arc in the Midland Valley, which lay above a south-east-dipping subduction zone. However, arc magmatism continued until 20 Ma after the climax of the Grampian Orogeny, suggesting a flip in the direction of subduction to northwards beneath the Midland Valley Terrane, after its collision with Laurentia. Metamorphic clasts and xenoliths in Upper Paleozoic lavas of the Midland Valley further suggest that the Midland Valley Terrane formed on a sliver of older continental crust.

- The Highland Border Complex contains evidence for sedimentation until 25 Ma after the climax of the Grampian phase, and bears no sign of its effects. Neither it nor the Midland Valley Terrane contain any debris derived from the metamorphosed Dalradian, until the Late Ordovician. A partial explanation for these anomalies is that the Midland Valley Terrane slid laterally to the present north-east to dock with the Grampian Terrane, after its collision with Laurentia.

- Ordovician sediments of the Southern Uplands occur in several blocks bounded by southward-directed thrusts. The stratigraphy from block to block shows increasing duration of deep-water deposition towards the south. The combination of both regional features suggests that the Southern Uplands Terrane formed as an accretionary prism above a northwards subduction zone.

5.2.3 Events in the South

Through the Cambrian to Early Ordovician, the northern British Isles were accumulating varied kinds of sediment in four distinct terranes (Hebridean, Grampian, Midland Valley and Southern Uplands). Figure 5.12 shows the stratigraphic record in Avalonia during the Cambrian and Ordovician.

- Compared with what you might expect from Figure 3.7a and Section 5.1.2, what seems to be missing from the Cambrian of Avalonia in Figure 5.12?

- There are no volcanic lavas from 545 to 490 Ma, although there is volcanic debris in turbidites. Yet paleomagnetic data show that Avalonia was still an integral part of Gondwana, specifically the Cadomian volcanic arc above a subduction zone that dipped beneath the supercontinent.

- In plate-tectonic terms, can you suggest what might have been happening on the Gondwana side of the Iapetus Ocean during the Cambrian?

- Subduction beneath Gondwana must have stopped before the start of the Cambrian, at least where the British part of Avalonia was situated.

Assuming that the inertia of Gondwana was, like that of Eurasia today, too large for plate forces to shift it as fast as the rate of sea-floor spreading in Iapetus, the main spreading centre may have moved away from Gondwana. Throughout the Cambrian, there is no evidence for subduction beneath the major continents on either side of Iapetus. However, the evidence from the Midland Valley Terrane indicates that subduction to create an oceanic arc did take place.

Figure 5.12 shows that in Wales the oldest Ordovician rocks contain typical arc volcanics, so subduction did restart beneath Avalonia. However, in case you get the idea that the British part of Avalonia was a mass of active volcanoes, as are the modern volcanic arcs of Indonesia and the Andes, study the Ordovician stratigraphy in Figure 5.12 and attempt Question 5.4.

> Question 5.4 Summarize the changing environments during the Ordovician for (a) south-east Ireland; (b) Wales; (c) Shropshire; and (d) the Lake District.

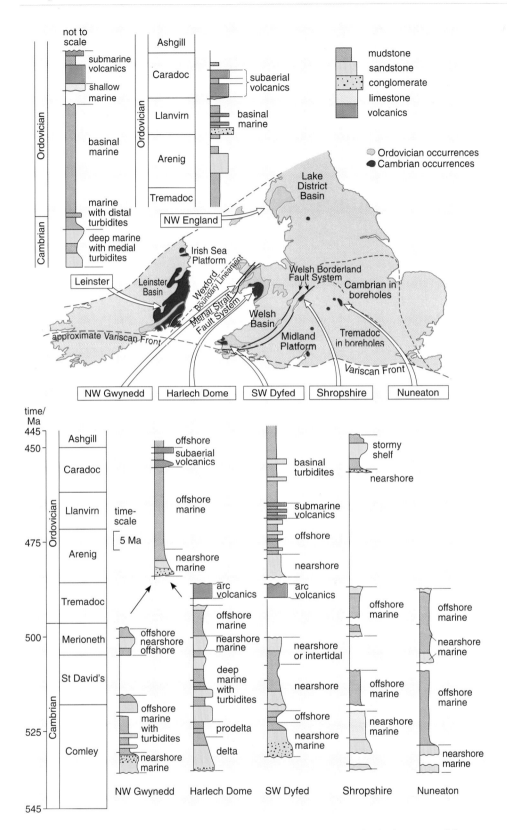

Figure 5.12 Sedimentary sequences from the Cambrian and Early Ordovician of the southern British Isles. (*Note:* The vertical axis of the stratigraphic sections represents time, not thickness.)

The overall picture is one dominated by marine sedimentation. Volcanism occurred at different times in different places in this tiny area. Moreover, only in North Wales and the Lake District are there any volcanic rocks that erupted on dry land to resemble those of a modern volcanic arc. The British record does not support continual volcanic activity throughout the Ordovician. Yet there is little doubt that subduction must have continued beneath Avalonia from the start of the Ordovician, so that north and south parts of the British Isles eventually merged. Otherwise, how could the Iapetus Ocean have disappeared?

- How might this apparent paradox be resolved?

- Modern arc volcanoes are spectacular edifices, but they are *high* and therefore prone to rapid erosion. Subaerial volcanism stands little chance of long-term preservation except as relics. Material in subaerial stratovolcanoes eventually finds its way to the sea as debris that contributes to turbidites. Almost certainly that is the case for the Ordovician of Avalonia, much of which lay offshore of a volcanic arc.

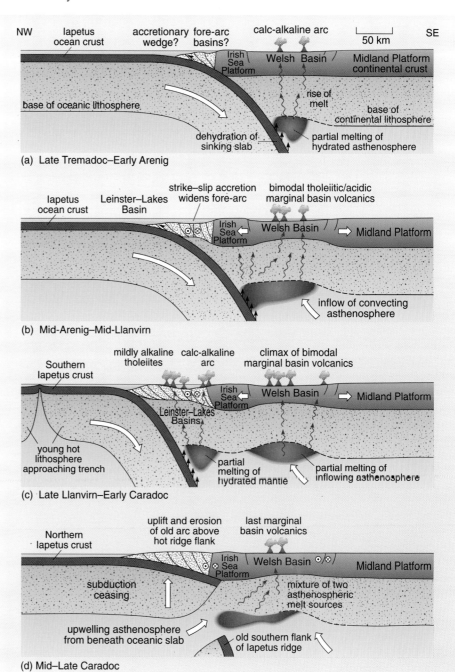

Figure 5.13 Schematic cross-sections through the northern margin of Avalonia for different times in the Ordovician Period, as the leading edge of the microcontinent extended oceanwards through formation of an accretionary prism. Refer to Figure 5.12 for the epochs that make up the Ordovician Period and for the stratigraphic evidence that supports the various stages. Circles with dots or crosses indicate lateral movement out of or into the page, respectively. In (a), accretionary wedge = accretionary prism.

Many geologists have taken the stratigraphic position of Ordovician lavas and pyroclastic rocks at face value to erect intricate scenarios for how volcanism was controlled. There are indeed petrographic and geochemical differences between the Ordovician volcanic rocks of different areas and ages. They suggest influences over the style of partial melting at the subduction zone that evolved as the lithosphere above it changed (Figure 5.13).

Compared with the volumes of volcanic rocks in modern volcanic arcs, those of Ordovician age in the southern British Isles seem scanty, probably as a result of continual erosion and reworking to form turbidites. So the evolving scenario in Figure 5.13 needs to be viewed with caution. The areas of Ordovician outcrop are also very small, being hidden by later cover of Silurian to Tertiary age. Quite possibly that masks more voluminous Ordovician volcanic rocks and the calc-alkaline intrusions that would have underpinned major volcanoes. If you examine MAG (Section 2) in the area of Younger Cover in eastern England, you will see a great deal of 'roughness', and many areas show magnetic highs. Some may be such buried volcanic centres of the Ordovician arc.

Apart from a few occurrences of volcanic rocks in Ireland and south-west Wales, the succeeding Silurian Period reveals a picture of sedimentation alone, continuous in mid-Wales and the Lake District, but only getting underway during the Late Silurian in other areas. Figure 5.14 shows how geography probably evolved after volcanism and subduction beneath Avalonia ceased. Evolution towards dry land was completed by the beginning of the Devonian for the whole of the British Isles, except to the south of the Variscan Front.

Figure 5.13 suggests that the axis of spreading of the Iapetus Ocean disappeared by subduction beneath Avalonia towards the end of the Ordovician Period. One half of the oceanic lithosphere produced by that spreading remains to be accounted for. Some would have been subducted northwards beneath the Midland Valley and Southern Uplands Terranes during the Late Ordovician, but paleomagnetic data indicate significant separation between northern and southern parts of the British Isles at that time. The absence of Silurian volcanic rocks, throughout eastern North America as well as the British Isles, poses a problem.

5.2.4   Caledonian continental collision

The building of the Southern Uplands Terrane involved turbidite sedimentation until the Early Silurian and its tectonic incorporation in an accretionary prism. Silurian sediments also poured over the Midland Valley Terrane, but most of them are non-marine. The upper part of the Silurian sequence there is dominated by conglomerates formed in alluvial fans. Sedimentary structures show debris transported from the south-east, opposite to the sediment transport during the Ordovician. These sediments are tectonically crucial, for up to 80% of the clasts in them are igneous rocks, ranging from oceanic basalts to arc-type mafic and felsic materials, but none have been dated. This is indirect evidence for yet another high-relief volcanic arc that shed copious debris, that lay somewhere between the present Southern Uplands Fault and the Solway. That 'somewhere' is nowhere to be seen today, and has either been tectonically buried by thrusting, or moved 'somewhere else' by major strike–slip faulting. It seems likely to have been a volcanic arc, generated by continued northward subduction of the remains of Iapetus Ocean lithosphere.

Your study of the tectonic evolution of the West Pacific through the Cenozoic (Block 1, Activity 1.2) shows that strike–slip 'shuffling' of oceanic arcs and their docking against larger continental masses is an important aspect of modern plate tectonics. Particularly instructive is the way in which New Guinea was assembled, and you may wish to run the CD animation of the West Pacific

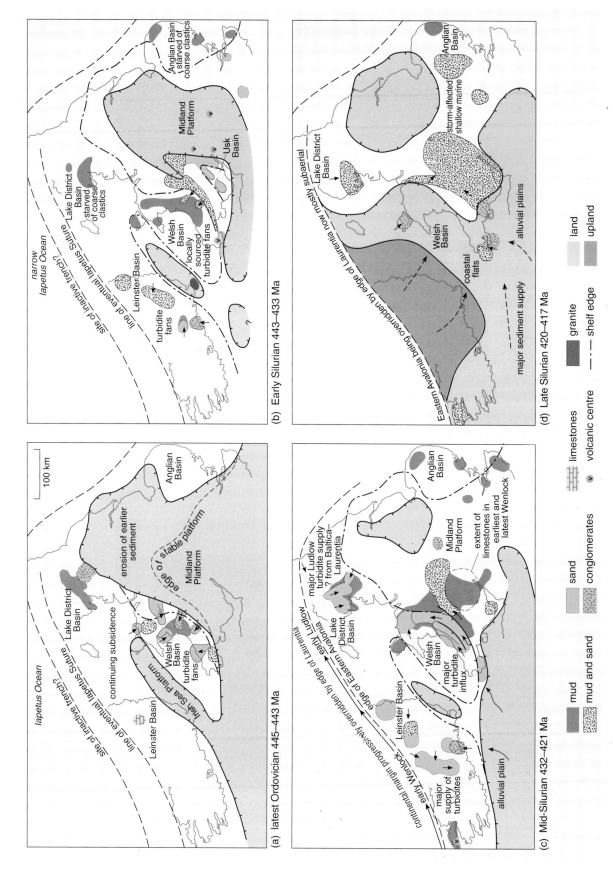

Figure 5.14 Paleogeographic maps of the southern British Isles from the latest Ordovician until the end of the Silurian.

again. Equally, much of Alaska and British Columbia assembled by such docking of far-travelled terranes during the Mesozoic (Block 1, Figure 1.15). Strike–slip tectonics was almost certainly involved in the creation of the British lithosphere during the Lower Paleozoic Era, but evidence for it is subtle and largely obscured by later sedimentation.

From your earlier studies, you might remember the concept of the 'Old Red Sandstone' continent, of which the British Isles were a part, and which came into being after the final closure of the Iapetus Ocean. It existed throughout the Devonian Period, and formed by collision of the Avalonia microcontinent with Laurentia. Assessing when this final event of the Caledonian Orogeny (this is referred to as the **Acadian** phase in Block 4, Section 3.1) took place relies on the timing of the structures that it produced. Figure 5.15 shows the evidence from the British Isles.

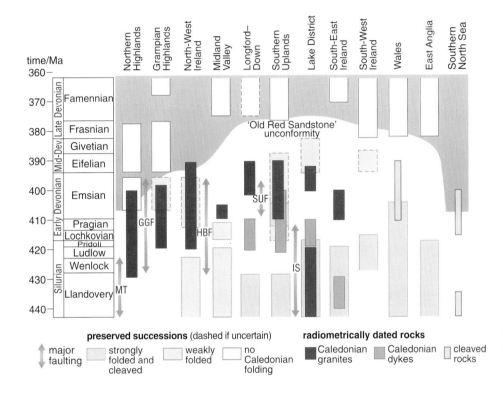

Figure 5.15 Ages of sedimentary rocks containing evidence of folding and cleavage formation and those that do not in various parts of the British Isles. The chart also shows the radiometric age spans of felsic intrusions, and durations of major faulting. MT Moine Thrust; GGF Great Glen Fault; HBF Highland Boundary Fault; SUF Southern Uplands Fault; IS Iapetus Suture.

Question 5.5 Does the information shown by Figure 5.15 indicate that Acadian deformation occurred everywhere at the same time? (Remember that development of cleavage suggests intense deformation, whereas folding alone represents weaker buckling.) If not, where did it end first and where last?

Because of the widely varying timing of Acadian deformation, the unconformity that represents the erosion of the newly thickened and elevated crust is not a time plane, but occurs at different times across the British Isles. The tectonic significance of this is difficult to judge. Figure 5.14c suggests that the Avalonia–Laurentia collision was oblique so that contact progressed north-eastwards along the northern flank of Avalonia. Such oblique docking of irregular continental margins could explain the diachronous nature of the 'Old Red' unconformity.

The clearest feature shown by Figure 5.15 is that over most of the orogen both granitic plutons and felsic dykes punctured the newly assembled crust, between 430 to 390 Ma (Late Silurian to Middle Devonian). There is no discernible difference in this respect between northern and southern parts of the British Isles. This massive pulse of felsic magmatism is the topic of Section 5.4.

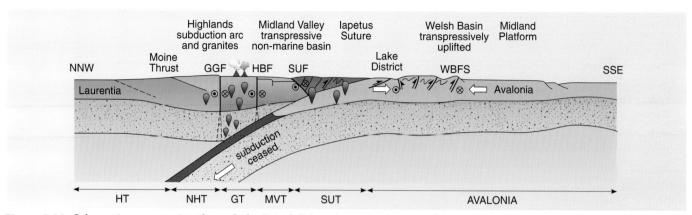

Figure 5.16 Schematic cross-section through the British lithosphere after its assembly in Late Silurian to Early Devonian times. Circles with dots or crosses indicate lateral movement out of or into the page, respectively. Terranes with clearly distinct infrastructures appear in different shades: HT Hebridean Terrane (pink); NHT Northern Highlands Terrane (orange); GT Grampian Terrane (mauve); MVT Midland Valley Terrane (light green); SUT Southern Uplands Terrane (dark green); Avalonia (pale blue). Faults: GGF Great Glen Fault; HBF Highland Boundary Fault; SUF Southern Uplands Fault; WBFS Welsh Borderland Fault System. See also Figure 2.10.

Despite abundant granitic intrusions throughout the British Isles, rocks involved in the Acadian collision of Avalonia with Scotland and northern Ireland are barely metamorphosed, except in the thermal aureoles of the granites. Unlike the products of the Grampian phase, which reached metamorphic grades capable of melting the crust at shallow levels (Block 4, Figure 6.21), rocks deformed by Acadian events only reached pressures and temperatures of prehnite–pumpellyite grade (Block 4, Figure 6.22). Neither huge nappes nor major thrusts were able to produce abnormally thickened crust.

Figure 5.16 completes your progress through the assembly of the British lithosphere up to the end of the Silurian, showing a schematic cross-section though it from north-north-west to south-south-east. It incorporates some of the elements derived from seismic studies that you met in Section 2 (Figure 2.10).

5.2.5   Summary of Sections 5.2.3 and 5.2.4

- The absence of volcanic rocks from the Cambrian of Avalonia, at a time when it was still part of Gondwana, implies that subduction beneath the supercontinent had ceased, so that the Cadomian volcanic arc became quiescent. Volcanism restarted in the Ordovician, as Avalonia drifted away from Gondwana, yet the volume of volcanic rocks is small relative to that of Ordovician turbidite sediments. This is probably because subaerial arc volcanoes were rapidly eroded, thereby supplying debris to submarine turbidity flows.

- Although intricate scenarios have been suggested for the evolution of Ordovician volcanism, to account for its appearance at various times in different parts of the southern British Isles and geographic differences in lava composition, such hypotheses need to be viewed with caution.

- The Silurian is dominated by marine sedimentary rocks. However, sedimentation was only continuous in mid-Wales and the Lake District, spreading further afield in the Late Silurian, and becoming terrestrial by the end of the period. The absence of Silurian volcanic rocks suggests that lithosphere of the Iapetus Ocean remaining at the end of the Ordovician was not subducted beneath the southern British Isles.

- Silurian terrestrial sediments of the Scottish Midland Valley contain abundant volcanic clasts with arc affinities. There are no such materials in the Scottish Highlands, and sediment transport directions are from the south-east. So, these volcanic clasts came from an arc, for which the geology of the British Isles shows no evidence. This elusive volcanic arc may have resulted from the final northward subduction of Iapetus. The most reasonable explanation is that the arc was moved away from a position close to southern Scotland by large strike–slip movements. It is even possible that the Southern Uplands Terrane was thrust *en masse* over the missing source for the volcanic clasts in the Silurian.

- The final closure of Iapetus, and the docking of Avalonia with the terranes of the northern British Isles climaxed in the Acadian phase of the Caledonian Orogeny. Thereafter, the assembled continent rose above sea-level to become the 'Old Red Continent', which resulted in a profound unconformity (Figure 2.1b). Rather than being a 'time-plane', the unconformity has sediments of different ages above rocks deformed by the Grampian and Acadian phases. These cover an age range of more than 20 Ma, from Early to Late Devonian. Rather than charting variation in time of the final event in the Caledonian Orogeny across the British Isles, the age of the 'Old Red' unconformity reflects the time at which sedimentation began to outweigh erosion and transport of debris from uplifted crust.

- The dates of igneous intrusions into the newly welded British crust, and less well-constrained ages of episodes that deformed it, suggest that the final, Acadian phase of the Caledonian Orogeny occurred at different times (from 430–382 Ma) in different places. This evidence for diachronous tectonics probably reflects two factors: the assembly of terranes with irregular margins, and protracted strike–slip movement along terrane boundaries.

5.3   Regional tectonics during the Lower Paleozoic Era

Section 3 summarized developments in global tectonics during the Lower Paleozoic (Figure 3.7). Having worked your way through evidence for the assembly of the various terranes that comprise the British Isles, this is an appropriate point to revisit the regional picture. Figure 5.17 shows Cambrian to Late Silurian paleogeographic and tectonic maps for the area that now forms the borders of the North Atlantic. The paleogeographic maps are artist's impressions that roughly mimic the shaded-relief maps that you met in Blocks 2, 3 and 4. The continental architectures of the borderlands of the North Atlantic are the best studied anywhere, although there are still many unresolved aspects of their Lower Paleozoic evolution. Some Earth scientists disagree with the details in Figure 5.17, and there are bound to be revisions as more information is assembled.

The maps use names for several assemblies of continental crust, large island arc terranes and inferred oceans that are internationally recognized (Figure 5.17f). Most will be new to you, and will not be assessed. However, publications with a wider scope than the British Isles use them, and they are increasingly referred to in papers about our own small 'snapshot' of global evolution.

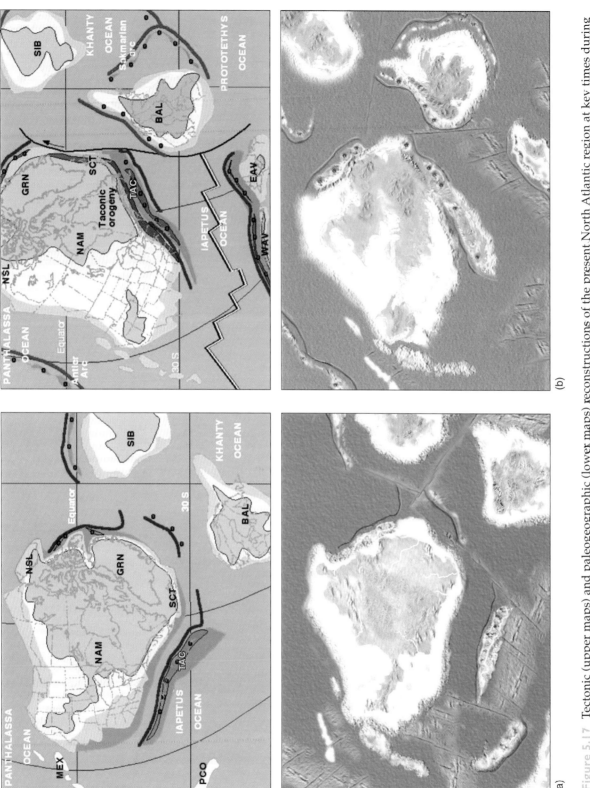

Figure 5.17 Tectonic (upper maps) and paleogeographic (lower maps) reconstructions of the present North Atlantic region at key times during the Lower Paleozoic Era. (a) Middle Cambrian (510 Ma); (b)

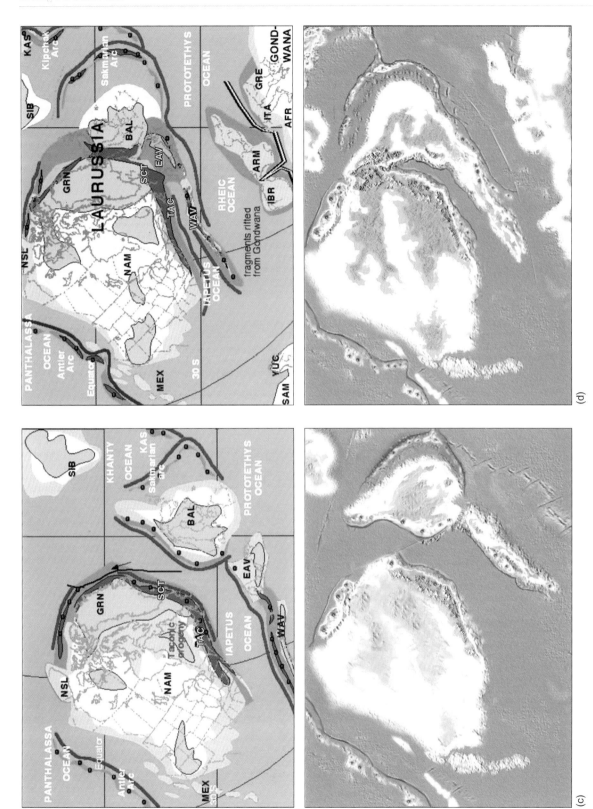

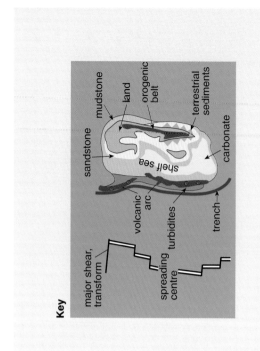

Key

major shear, transform

spreading centre

sandstone

shelf sea

land

mudstone

orogenic belt

terrestrial sediments

carbonate

volcanic arc

turbidites

trench

List of plates and abbreviations

ARA	Arabia	MEX	Mexico
AFR	Africa	MEG	Meguma (East US)
ARM	Armorica (South Europe)	NAM	North America
BAL	Baltica (North Europe)	NSL	North Slope (Alaska)
EAV	East Avalonia (England)	PCO	Precordillera (Andes)
FLA	Florida	SAM	South America
GRE	Greece	SCT	Scotland
GRN	Greenland	SIB	Siberia
IBR	Iberia (Spain Portugal)	TAC	Taconia (East US)
IRA	Iran	TUR	Turkey
ITA	Italy	WAV	West Avalonia (East US)
KAS	Kazakhstan (central Asia)	YUC	Yucatan

(f)

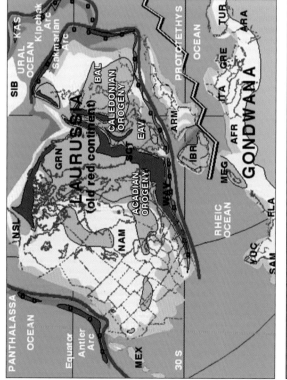

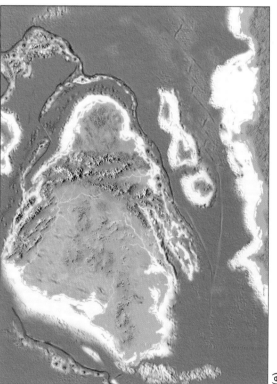

(e)

Figure 5.17a shows the overall situation in the Middle Cambrian. Notice that there are several volcanic arcs associated with subduction zones and trenches — the direction of subduction is from the trench towards (and beneath) the volcanoes shown as red dots. In the context of the British Isles, the most important is that labelled TAC (Taconia), which is represented very clearly by a terrane with Cambrian to Early Ordovician arc volcanics in eastern Canada and the USA.

● Which terrane in Scotland might be part of Taconia?

● The Midland Valley Terrane, although the evidence there for arc volcanism is indirect.

The sense of subduction to the SSW beneath Taconia fits with that inferred for the Midland Valley Terrane. The narrow strip of ocean floor between Taconia and Laurentia was destined to close. You should note that the ocean-ridge system in the Iapetus Ocean would have been driving Taconia to a 'head-to-head' collision with Laurentia.

● How would Taconia have approached Scotland (SCT — at this time the Grampian Terrane)?

● The edge of Laurentia in the vicinity of Scotland is not parallel to the ridge shown on the paleogeographic map, and so you would anticipate an oblique approach involving sinistral strike–slip motion. The paleogeographic map shows a major strike–slip fault trending SE–NW past SCT.

Figure 5.17b represents the time of the Grampian phase of the Caledonian Orogeny in the northern British Isles — the climax of Dalradian deformation and metamorphism. Taconia had begun to collide with North America, initiating the Taconic Orogeny there, of which the Grampian phase is a small representative in the British Isles (the different nomenclature either side of the modern Atlantic reflects the fact that both were named before anyone knew that they were of the same age, rather than any national pride). Your prediction of regional strike–slip movements with a sinistral sense tallies with a huge oceanic shear zone along which Baltica was travelling obliquely towards East Greenland. The sense of subduction beneath Taconia had flipped, as also suggested by Late Ordovician volcanic clasts in the debris shed by the Midland Valley Terrane (Figure 5.8). The subduction zone was the site of accretionary-prism formation in what was to become the Southern Uplands Terrane (Figure 5.9). Avalonia makes its appearance to the south. Subduction beneath its northern edge, represented by the Middle Ordovician volcanism of the Lake District, signifies that the Iapetus Ocean had begun to close by consumption of oceanic lithosphere at both its margins.

By the Late Ordovician (Figure 5.17c), ocean closure and strike–slip movements brought Baltica and Avalonia ever closer to contact with a vast mountain range formed along the now south-eastern edge of Laurentia by the Grampian-Taconic orogenic event. Another major spreading centre had come into play (Prototethys), driving Baltica and Avalonia to the NNW. About 20 Ma later, during the Early Silurian (Figure 5.17d), Iapetus was almost closed. Baltica had docked obliquely against the East Greenland margin of Laurentia to form **Laurussia**, and eastern Avalonia was close to collision with Scotland. The two were separated by a narrow sea into which clastic debris was pouring from both sides, to form terrestrial sediments in the Midland Valley, and marine muds and turbidites over much of Wales and northern England (SE England and the Low Countries are shown as a landmass). An important feature in both Figure 5.17c and 5.17d is the inference of prolonged sinistral strike–slip along the zone separating Baltica and East Avalonia from Greenland and Scotland. The many terranes that constitute much of the British Isles docked obliquely with Laurentia, sliding components of the lithosphere together in the manner of a sheared pack of cards. In the case of eastern North America, the approaching collision was to be head-to-head, to initiate the Acadian Orogeny, again roughly synchronous with the last phase of the Caledonian Orogeny in the British Isles, which bears the same name, and in Scandinavia (where it is referred to as the Scandian event).

During the Early Silurian (Figure 5.17d), Gondwana lost another piece of territory, comprising what was to become most of central Europe and the Iberian Peninsula, in the form of Armorica. A new constructive margin formed beneath northern Gondwana, to spall off this small, drifting continent, leaving southern Europe behind, for the time being. The Lower Paleozoic was soon to end, with the shrinkage of the Rheic Ocean, now lacking a constructive margin and being subducted beneath the SSE edge of Avalonia.

By the Early Devonian (Figure 5.17e), Laurussia was almost surrounded by destructive plate margins; it was destined to grow during the Upper Paleozoic. To the mountain chain formed by the Grampian–Taconic event had been added yet more highlands, because of the collision of Avalonia around 400 Ma. Subduction of the Rheic Ocean beneath Laurussia generated a long continental volcanic arc, in many ways analogous to that along the modern Andes (Block 3). It is to that subduction-related magmatism that we now turn.

5.3.1   Summary of Section 5.3

- During the Cambrian, the Scottish Midland Valley was part of the Taconia island arc, beneath which Iapetus lithosphere was being subducted. This arc collided head-on with Laurentia, during the Taconic Orogeny of eastern North America. Where the Midland Valley Terrane collided with Laurentia, motion was oblique, leading to a sinistral, strike–slip component during the Grampian phase of the Caledonian Orogeny ('Grampian' and 'Taconic' are synonymous for this region).

- Avalonia entered the scene on the opposite side of the Iapetus spreading centre, and by the time of the Grampian–Taconic orogenic event in Laurentia, subduction was passing beneath it and Laurentia — Iapetus began to close more rapidly. Throughout the Ordovician, the northern edge of Avalonia was a volcanic arc.

- Around the end of the Ordovician, the Iapetus spreading centre had been subducted. Spreading of the Paleotethys Ocean (between Gondwana and both Avalonia and Baltica, and connected to the Rheic Ocean) was then able to drive the remnant of the Iapetus Ocean to final closure in the Early Silurian. In the vicinity of the British Isles, plate motions remained oblique to the Laurentian margin. This added further sinistral strike–slip motion to the eventual docking of the British Isles' terranes, in a similar fashion to the Mesozoic processes that caused accretion of much of western North America and those of more recent times which have dominated the evolution of the West Pacific (Block 1).

- Three large slivers (Taconia, Avalonia and Armorica) split from Gondwana during the Paleozoic, by successive initiation of sea-floor spreading at its margin, in a way that is reminiscent of the modern East African Rift and Red Sea (Block 2). The last of these to part company, Armorica, constituted what was to become most of southern Europe, with the exception of Greece and Italy. Its docking with the growing mass of Laurussia was in the Late Carboniferous Period.

• The 'Old Red Continent' of Laurussia, of which most of the British Isles formed a peripheral part, was enveloped by subduction zones. Not only was it destined to grow by further accretion, but its lithosphere continually experienced compressive stress. It was unable to extend to form sedimentary basins. Instead, it shed masses of debris and accumulated a veneer of terrestrial or shallow-marine sediments until the end of the Paleozoic Era.

5.4   Spot-welding of the Iapetus Suture zone

Figure 5.15 shows that emplacement of granitic plutons and felsic dykes accompanied the Acadian phase of the Caledonian Orogeny in the British Isles. They are present in most of the terranes, except Wales, south-west England and south-west Ireland. None of them is younger than 390 Ma, and the oldest is 440 Ma, i.e. they are of Silurian to Early Devonian age. The Moine Thrust cuts one of the oldest of these granites, thereby revealing that the thrust was active in Silurian times, at around 425 Ma — it is a late Caledonian structure, formed well within Laurentia. You can judge the abundance and distribution of Caledonian granites from Figure 5.18. The dense cluster in the Grampian Terrane probably reflects the depth to which subsequent erosion has penetrated. As you found in Section 2.1, even where the Older and Younger Cover veneer the British Isles' surface, such granitic rocks affect patterns in the geophysical potential field maps, particularly GRAV, and occur extensively beneath northern and eastern England, to the south of the Iapetus Suture.

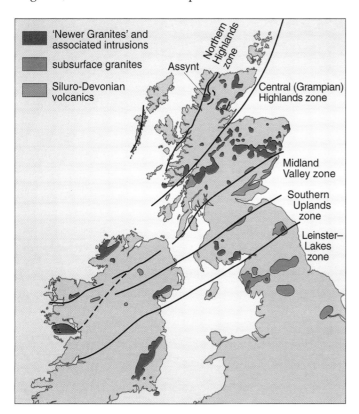

Figure 5.18 Distribution of Silurian to Devonian granitic intrusions (red). Purple shows those detected using geophysical techniques. Green shows exposures of Early Devonian volcanic rocks.

Early Devonian volcanic rocks occur exclusively to the north of the suture, and consist of dominantly andesitic to felsic lavas and tuffs, with some basaltic flows that are silica-saturated or oversaturated. These compositions fit with magmatism related to subduction towards the present north-west, as expected from Figure 5.16. Their high initial $^{87}Sr/^{86}Sr$ ratios (0.708 to 0.730) indicate that a crustal component was assimilated in their parent magma. The granites at Ben

Nevis, in Glencoe and the Cheviots, occur in direct contact with the lavas. That at Glencoe contains foundered masses of lavas and reveals annular faults, which show that it formed beneath a caldera.

Magmas of granitic composition generally form above subduction zones by a mixture of mantle melting, fractional crystallization and some assimilation of older crust (Block 3, Section 4).

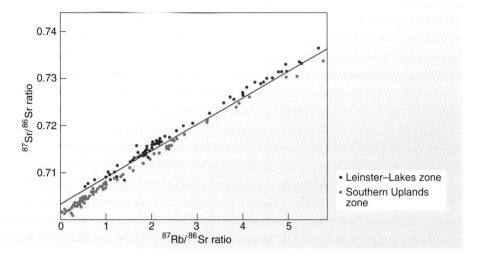

Figure 5.19 Rubidium and strontium isotopes plotted for granitic rocks from north (Southern Uplands Terrane) and south (Leinster–Lakes Terrane) of the Iapetus Suture. The black line is a line of 'best fit' through all the data — it is not an isochron.

⬤ Figure 5.19 shows plots of ^{87}Sr/^{86}Sr against ^{87}Rb/^{86}Sr for rocks collected from Caledonian granitic complexes either side of the suggested position of the Iapetus Suture. (Note this is not an isochron diagram, because several plutons of slightly different ages contribute to it.) What can you conclude about the source of the granites?

⬤ The plots for granites north of the suture intercept the ^{87}Sr/^{86}Sr axis at about 0.702. This is around the value that geochemists would expect to characterize mantle materials 400 Ma ago, and indicates that the magmas had not assimilated crustal material. Those from south of the suture have a significantly higher value (0.705) indicating either some assimilation or a mantle source that was slightly enriched in Rb.

The very existence of granites of this age in former Avalonia, south of the Iapetus Suture, poses a problem. Strontium isotopes suggest that their parent magmas formed as a result of wedge melting above a subduction zone, yet, according to Figure 5.16, there was no such thing beneath Avalonia during the Devonian. This has vexed some of the finest minds in isotope geochemistry and tectonics. Perhaps subduction of the Rheic Ocean had begun beneath southern Avalonia as Armorica moved northwards, but there is no structural evidence for that in the southern British Isles. In Blocks 1 and 4 (Section 7.4.4), you considered the process of delamination or convective thinning of the lithosphere to account for aspects of the uplift of the Tibetan Plateau and post-collision magmatism there. One possible, though unproveable, explanation for the Caledonian granites of the southern British Isles is that part of the subducted Iapetus lithosphere delaminated to be replaced by asthenosphere, thereby heating the subcontinental lithosphere and generating the magmas from which these granites evolved.

5.4.1 Summary of Section 5.4

• Following the complete closure of the Iapetus Ocean during the Acadian phase of the Caledonian Orogeny, partial melting in the mantle beneath almost all of the British Isles generated magmas typical of volcanic arcs. They formed extensive lavas in the Midland Valley and Grampian Terranes during the Early Devonian, but the most pervasive igneous rocks are granitic intrusions. Their strontium-isotope compositions show that the magmas assimilated some continental crust south of the Iapetus Suture, but remained pristine products of mantle processes to the north.

• Magmatism with arc affinities that follows terrane amalgamation and orogeny is odd. That is particularly so for the Devonian British Isles, because the further from the southern flank of Avalonia (where subduction of the Rheic Ocean might conceivably have been going on), the more volcanic and intrusive rocks there are. A plausible speculation is that convective thinning of the lithosphere induced magmatism.

5.5 Final assembly: the Variscan Orogeny

Your study of the Tectonic Map and seismic reflection profiles across SW England in Section 2.2.2 revealed the Variscan Front, the northern limit of northward thrusting around the end of the Carboniferous (Figure 2.14). The Variscan Orogeny, and its rough time equivalents, the Hercynian and Appalachian Orogenies in central Europe and eastern North America, resulted from a series of collisions of several microplates with Laurussia (Figure 5.20). Figure 5.17e shows Iberia and Amorica separated from Gondwana by a constructive margin. By the end of the Carboniferous, they had amalgamated with northern Europe, accompanied by Siberia that had docked from the east along the line of the Ural Suture. The addition of Gondwana from the south to the rapidly growing crustal mass formed Pangaea, with a huge mountain range roughly along the Equator. The British Isles' contribution to understanding the final assembly of this titanic supercontinent, which was to dominate the next 100 Ma, is the geology of SW England.

5.5.1 Variscan evolution in SW England

Throughout the Devonian and Carboniferous, south-western England, formerly part of Avalonia, lay at the southern edge of the 'Old Red Continent'. The sedimentary evolution of Devon and Cornwall involved the successive development and closure of rift-related basins, into which poured sediment derived from the subaerial continent to the north (South Wales) and from a growing accretionary prism to the south. The Devonian sequence, mainly marine, contains submarine basaltic lavas that possibly represent back-arc extension associated with the northward subduction zone shown on Figure 5.17e. Carboniferous sedimentation was dominated by turbidites, known locally as 'Culm', whose sedimentary structures indicate turbidity currents flowing northwards from a major source of debris in the region of the present English Channel.

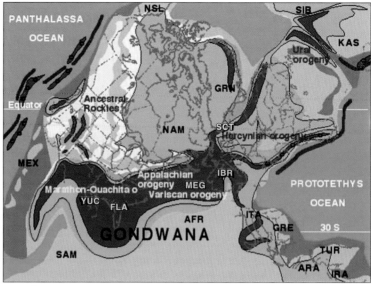

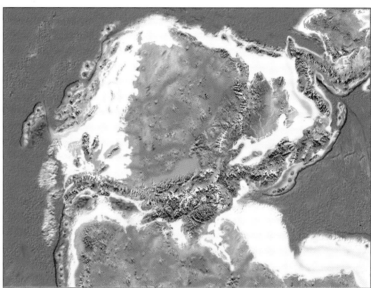

Figure 5.20 Tectonic and paleogeographic reconstruction of the present North Atlantic region during the Late Carboniferous (300 Ma). See Figure 5.17f for the key to ornaments and abbreviations. Images kindly provided by Ronald Blakey, Northern Arizona University, USA. Full-size versions are included on the Block 3 CD.

The Variscan Front (Section 2.2.2) is not a suture, but the northward limit of deformation of Avalonia during the Variscan Orogeny. Sutures are typically marked by ophiolites obducted during collision. On GRAV (Section 2.1), the southernmost part of SW England (the Lizard and Start Point peninsulas) shows a marked positive Bouguer anomaly.

⬤ Can you see anything that might be responsible for this gravity high on the Tectonic Map?

⬤ The Lizard Peninsula of South Cornwall has dense mafic and ultramafic rocks in an ophiolite known as the Lizard Complex.

The Lizard Complex combines deep-marine sediments, Early Devonian pillow lavas, dyke swarms, gabbros and altered peridotite. Although tectonically disrupted, the complex is a classic ophiolite. The hydrous sheet silicate serpentine has replaced olivine in the peridotite. Serpentine is named because of its mottled appearance, reminiscent of a snake skin, and the most common variety of serpentine is lizardite, named after the Lizard Peninsula where it was first identified. (Incidentally, the name 'Lizard' has no connection with reptilian markings — it is derived from 'lezou', the Cornish word for headland.)

The geochemistry of pillow lavas in the Lizard ophiolite resembles MORB (Block 2, Section 2.6.3). The thrust on Figure 2.14c and d carried the ophiolite northwards over Devonian marine sediments, which resulted in their high-grade metamorphism at 360 Ma (Late Devonian). Some geologists interpret this as evidence for a subduction zone dipping southward beneath the northern margin of Armorica, and that the Lizard Complex marks the suture between Avalonia and Armorica. Paleomagnetic evidence is unable to separate the two terranes during Late Silurian to Middle Devonian times, and the maximum width of the Rheic Ocean then is thought to have been no more than 400 km.

It seems likely that Late Devonian closure of the Rheic Ocean initiated the Variscan Orogeny in SW England. However, sedimentation continued in Devon throughout the Carboniferous. Dominated by turbidites derived from the south, the 'Culm' is thought to have been deposited in a small foreland basin as debris from thickening and rising crust in Cornwall that was undergoing imbricate thrusting. Variscan deformation began in the 'Culm' basin during the Late Carboniferous, to form a pile of southward-verging nappes and a series of spectacular upright folds that developed at the close of Variscan deformation (Figure 5.21).

Figure 5.21 Tight, upright folds formed in the Carboniferous turbidites ('Culm') of North Devon during the Variscan Orogeny.

5.5.2 The Cornubian batholith

The 'backbone' of Cornwall is a series of five major granites that intrude folded Devonian and Carboniferous volcanics and sediments, and a few lesser plutons (Figure 5.22). These granites are known collectively as the **Cornubian batholith**, which was emplaced between 300 and 270 Ma. Their expression on GRAV is a series of large negative Bouguer anomalies (Section 2.1.1). Modelling of these anomalies, using appropriate densities for granite and the rocks that they intrude, suggests a single large body, with an estimated volume of 68 000 km^3, which extends from west of Land's End to Dartmoor in the east; like an iceberg, the Cornubian batholith is largely submerged (Figure 5.22b).

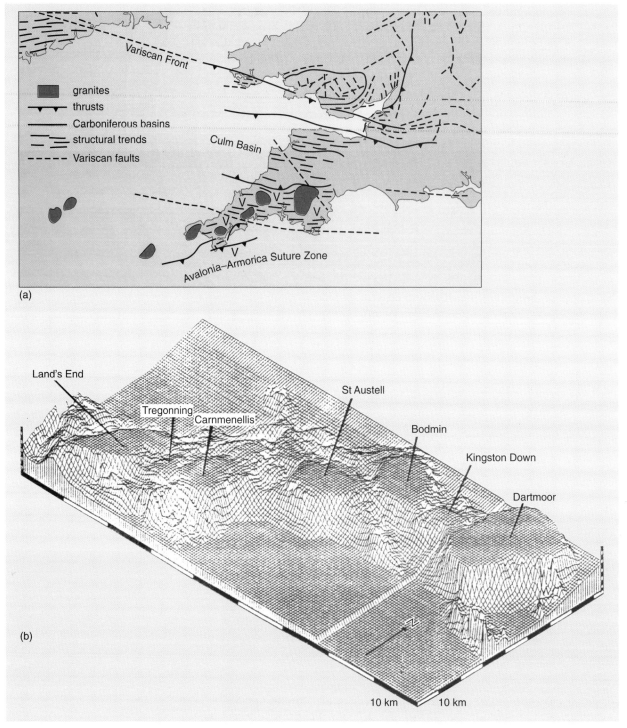

Figure 5.22 (a) Geological sketch-map of SW England. (b) Three-dimensional model showing the extent of the Cornubian batholith, derived from the local gravity anomalies.

The intrusions are undeformed, mostly muscovite–biotite granites that are often porphyritic. Cordierite is present in some of them. Lithium- and fluorine-rich granites, often containing abundant tourmaline, are common in areas where the once-valuable Cornish tin and copper ores developed.

Question 5.6　From the mineralogy and analyses of typical Cornubian granites (Table 5.1), suggest what geochemical type they are, and their likely tectonic setting.

Question 5.7 The initial $^{87}Sr/^{86}Sr$ isotope ratios of the granites are between 0.706 and 0.716, whereas those of the rocks that they intrude range from 0.709 to 0.721. At the time of intrusion, $^{87}Sr/^{86}Sr$ for the mantle was ~0.7035. Suggest a possible origin for the granite magma.

Table 5.1 Chemical and normative compositions of typical granites from the Cornubian batholith.

Oxides	(wt %)	(wt %)	(wt %)
SiO_2	71.73	72.43	73.70
TiO_2	0.25	0.21	0.06
Al_2O_3	14.55	15.03	14.10
Fe_2O_3	0.65	0.32	0.60
FeO	1.31	1.48	0.44
MnO	0.03	0.04	0.03
MgO	0.46	0.44	0.05
CaO	0.69	0.84	0.56
Na_2O	2.52	3.11	2.86
K_2O	5.50	5.06	4.77
P_2O_5	0.23	0.25	0.32
Total	97.92	99.21	97.49
Norm			
Q	33.8	32.2	38.3
Or	32.5	29.9	28.2
Ab	21.3	26.3	24.2
An	1.9	2.5	0.7
C	3.7	3.5	4.0
Hy	2.7	3.3	0.4
Mt	0.9	0.5	0.9
Il	0.5	0.4	0.1
Ap	0.5	0.6	0.7

Within the batholith, there are no components of intermediate compositions that might suggest an origin by fractional crystallization of mafic magma. The weight of evidence favours melting of deep crust with a lower Rb/Sr ratio than the exposed sediments.

● How does the Cornubian batholith compare with the High Himalayan leucogranites (Block 4, Section 7.5.3)?

● Geochemically, the Cornubian batholith is similar to the Himalayan leucogranites. Both are peraluminous granites associated with orogeny, and both probably formed by crustal melting.

Geochemistry alone does not show conclusively that two sets of granites formed in exactly the same way. There are two important clues related to your study of the evolution of the Tibetan Plateau during the Neogene (Block 4, Section 7), which should allow you to suggest a scenario for Carboniferous granite activity in Cornwall. First, in SW England, potassium-rich basaltic dykes and lava flows formed during and after granite emplacement. Secondly, the Cornubian batholith was emplaced after the Variscan Orogeny, when the crust was extending — there is evidence from seismic reflection surveys across the batholith that it has a flat base, perhaps on a major extensional detachment.

> Question 5.8 Bearing in mind these two observations, can you deduce a possible tectonic setting in which the Cornubian batholith was emplaced?

Although granites can form during active mountain building, as were the Himalayan leucogranites, or during active subduction (granite plutons of the Andean margin), many of the world's granites formed in a 'post-collisional' setting, for which convective thinning of the lithosphere is a plausible mechanism. This process may have generated both the Devonian granites south of the Iapetus Suture (Section 5.4), and the Cornubian batholith.

5.5.3 Summary of Section 5.5

- The Variscan Orogeny, together with similar events during the Late Carboniferous to Early Permian in North America, throughout Europe and in the Urals, marked the assembly of the supercontinent Pangaea. This united all older continental lithosphere, for the first time since the existence of Rodinia, about 700 Ma earlier.

- Although the Variscan Front, which outcrops from south-west Ireland to South Wales and is detectable further east beneath Younger Cover, is a profound structural boundary, it is not a suture zone. Much of the Devonian of Devon and Cornwall comprises marine sediments, derived from the 'Old Red Continent' to the present north, and lavas that may have formed in a back-arc basin. Carboniferous sedimentation involved turbidity flows that travelled northwards into a foreland basin from an accretionary prism close to a subduction zone.

- Seismic reflection and potential-field data suggest a major lithospheric boundary, probably a northwards thrust that affects the Moho, along the southern coast of England. Where these features occur onshore, they coincide with an ophiolite on the Lizard Peninsula, and high-grade metamorphic rocks at Start Point. The Lizard ophiolite has MORB affinities, and marks a terrane boundary, possibly that between Avalonia and Armorica.

- Several granite masses intruded the deformed Devonian and Carboniferous of Cornwall between 300 to 270 Ma. At depth, they coalesce as a regionally extensive body, the Cornubian batholith. Their peraluminous chemistry and high initial $^{87}Sr/^{86}Sr$ ratios show that the Cornish granites formed from magmas that had a high, if not total, content of crustal materials. Crustal melting may have been induced by heating that followed convective removal of the base of the lithosphere.

Objectives for Section 5

Now that you have completed this Section, you should be able to:

5.1   Understand the meaning of all the terms printed in **bold**.

5.2   Marshal evidence provided by igneous geochemistry, radiometric ages, clasts in sedimentary rocks, regional metamorphism in relation to major structures and igneous intrusions, and sequences of geological events to suggest tectonic environments which are represented in an area.

5.3   Relate local geological events to regional tectonic processes.

Question 5.9   What is the evidence that the Grampian and Northern Highland Terranes formed in separate tectonic settings?

Question 5.10 Why is it unlikely that the Dalradian Supergroup is a continuous sequence of sedimentary rocks?

Question 5.11 What kind of tectonic setting do the Ordovician and Silurian rocks of the Southern Uplands Terrane represent? Give a brief summary of the evidence.

Question 5.12 Why are the post-Caledonian granites and Devonian volcanic rocks anomalous relative to their setting?

Question 5.13 The Highland Border Complex has played an important role in understanding the evolution of the Laurentian part of the British Isles, despite its small occurrences. Name two processes that it helped to reveal.

Question 5.14 Which modern tectonic setting resembles the likely origins of Avalonia and Armorica in Gondwana?

Question 5.15 The British Isles have two major suites of granitic intrusion. What are their ages and how did they differ in their origins?

6 Episodes of extensional magmatism

Compared with the majestic events that led to the Paleozoic unification of the British Isles, those of later times are of little tectonic significance. For the most part, the British Isles became a passive receptacle for sediments of the Older and Younger Cover, whose deposition was subject to quirks inherited from its Variscan, Caledonian and older infrastructure. Basins, such as those of the North Sea and southern England, formed by extension of the lithosphere. The Mesozoic Wessex basin of southern England formed by extensional movements along originally Variscan thrust faults (on the Tectonic Map note the parallelism of the dark-green, normal faults there with the brown Variscan structures). It underwent tectonic inversion at about the same time as the Alpine Orogeny in southern Europe (Oligocene to Miocene — see the orange structural symbols on the Tectonic Map), so the earlier extensional structures became reverse faults and parts of the Wessex basin were folded. From the Permian onwards, the British Isles' crust lay deep within northern Pangaea, far from active plate boundaries. However, massive continental plates are not immune from far deeper processes, and Section 6 helps you to revise some of the skills learned in Block 2 by looking at intraplate volcanism, which occurred in the British Isles during the Carboniferous and Permian Periods, and at the outset of the Cenozoic Era, when the British Isles and Europe parted company with North America.

6.1 The Scottish Midland Valley

In this Section, you will explore the British expression of a pan-European magmatic event that began in the Early Carboniferous and continued until the Permian. This is the subject of active research, which aims to resolve uncertainties about the relationship of the magmatism to tectonics.

Towards the end of the Devonian, most of the crust of the British Isles was unified, but it was not stable. Caledonian orogenic events had left their imprint on the pre-Carboniferous basement as numerous lines of crustal weakness, which helped govern the accumulation of sediments and ascent of magmas during the Carboniferous. Figure 6.1 shows that the Scottish Midland Valley (SMV) became a graben some 80 km wide, bounded to the north by the

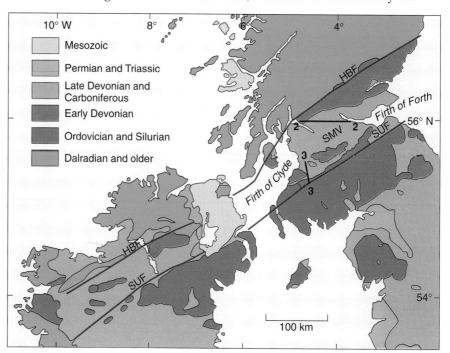

Figure 6.1 The Scottish Midland Valley dominated by Devonian and Carboniferous rocks in a NE–SW oriented graben. Lines 2–2 and 3–3 indicate lines of sections shown in Figures 6.2 and 6.3.

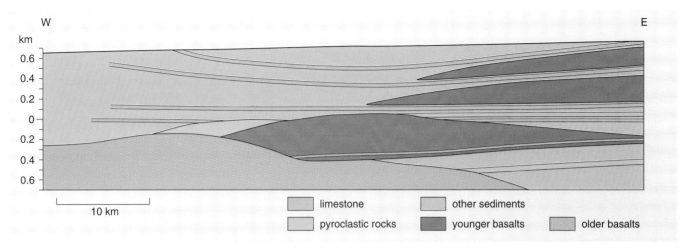

Figure 6.2   Interleaved Early Carboniferous sediments and lavas in the SMV along line 2–2 on Figure 6.1. For clarity, only limestone marker beds within the sedimentary lithologies are shown.

Highland Boundary Fault and to the south by the Southern Uplands Fault, both formed during Caledonian events. The original extent of the graben is not known, but its continuation south-westwards into Ireland suggests a minimum length of 500 km.

The SMV Carboniferous comprises a mixture of sedimentary rocks, up to 4 km thick, interleaved with numerous extrusive and intrusive igneous rocks (Figure 6.2).

> **Question 6.1**   What does this suggest about the relationship between sediment deposition and magmatism?

Subsidence suggests movement of the lithosphere. So can variations in sediment thicknesses shed light on how the lithosphere might have moved? Look at Figure 6.3, based on borehole data from the southern part of the SMV, near to the Southern Uplands Fault (line of section shown on Figure 6.1). Note the distinct increases in sediment thicknesses adjacent to faults.

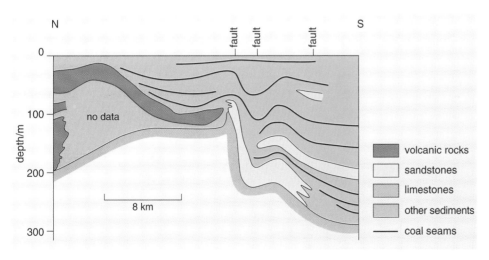

Figure 6.3   Cross-section towards the Southern Uplands Fault in SW Scotland, constructed from borehole data along line 3–3 on Figure 6.1. The section shows variations in sediment thickness associated with faults.

● What does this suggest about the activity and movement of the faults during deposition?

◐ These faults were active during deposition, and for thicker accumulations of sediments to occur they must have moved as normal faults.

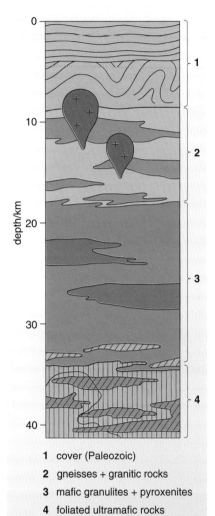

1   cover (Paleozoic)
2   gneisses + granitic rocks
3   mafic granulites + pyroxenites
4   foliated ultramafic rocks

Figure 6.4   Schematic interpretation of lithosphere structure below the Scottish Midland Valley, based on study of xenolith suites. Seismic velocities are deduced from the LISBP study (Section 2.2); layer 1 5–6 km s^{-1}, layer 2 >6.4 km s^{-1}, layer 3 ~7 km s^{-1}, layer 4 ~8 km s^{-1}.

Normal faulting controlled the deposition and accumulation of Carboniferous sediments throughout the SMV. Small, fault-bounded sedimentary basins are generally parallel to the main graben structure, which itself follows the dominant NE–SW trend of Caledonian structures. So it seems that pre-Carboniferous crustal weaknesses were reactivated during the evolution of the SMV.

Extensive and continuous normal faulting implies stretching and thinning of the lithosphere. Modelling of subsidence patterns in the SMV suggests that lithospheric extension (β) factors (Block 1, Section 3.4) were around 1.4. This is a significant amount of stretching and thinning, but complete failure of the SMV lithosphere did not occur, and the extension is comparable to that experienced by parts of the East African Rift System (Block 2, Sections 3 and 4).

The dominant Carboniferous sediments in the SMV are coals, sandstones, shales, and limestones, laid down in repeated cycles. Marine fossils occur mainly in the limestones.

● What can you conclude about the Carboniferous depositional environment in the SMV?

○ They are mainly terrestrial sediments, indicating deltaic and fluvial conditions. The presence of marine limestones suggests episodic seawater incursions and indicates that the SMV was near sea-level.

Very little pre-Devonian basement is exposed within the SMV (Figure 6.1), and its structure and composition must be gleaned from a combination of geophysical evidence and fragments of basement rocks (xenoliths) within Carboniferous volcanic rocks and intrusions. Figure 2.10 shows that thick crust lies beneath the sedimentary cover, and it is anomalously dense relative to crust to north and south (Section 2.2). Pre-Caledonian basement is inferred at shallow depths, and is itself underlain by a distinct lower crustal layer. The thin upper crustal layer is perhaps one reason for the unusually high gravitational potential over the SMV.

Xenoliths found in Carboniferous SMV volcanic vents fall into four categories: (i) Devonian and Carboniferous limestones, sandstones, and shales; (ii) mid-crustal xenoliths comprising various granites; (iii) lower crustal xenoliths, including gneisses, granulites, and yet more granites; (iv) mantle lithologies that comprise various ultramafic rocks.

Using the properties and compositions of these xenoliths, it is possible to construct a lithological interpretation of lithospheric structure beneath the SMV (Figure 6.4). This compares well with geophysical evidence (Figure 2.10) and matches rock types with seismic wave speeds. The SMV lithosphere comprises roughly 40 km of compositionally diverse rocks, the lower crust being mafic to ultramafic in composition.

6.1.1   Duration and extent of Carboniferous–Permian magmatism

Figure 6.5 shows how stratigraphic position of basaltic lavas in the SMV varies from west to east.

● Ignoring location, what does Figure 6.5 show in terms of the general pattern of igneous activity through time?

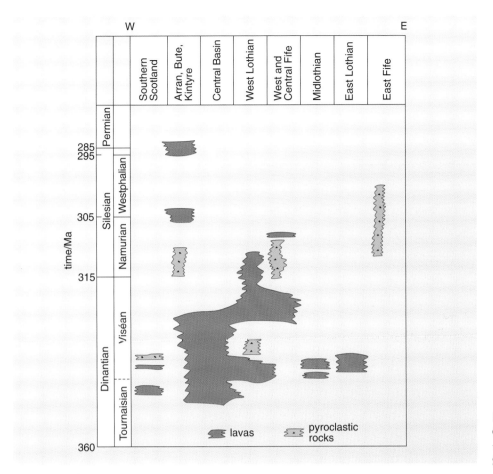

Figure 6.5 Stratigraphic summary of Carboniferous–Permian basaltic volcanism at various locations in the SMV. Intrusions are not shown.

● Although scattered across various locations in the SMV, igneous activity was continuous throughout the Carboniferous to the lower Permian with only a short break (*c.* 4–5 Ma) in the late Carboniferous.

Figure 6.5 does not show how magma productivity varied with time. Erosion has removed most of the original erupted volumes of basalt, but from what remains it is clear that 80–85% (>6000 km^3) was erupted during the Early Carboniferous. Eruption was not uniform across the SMV, so that thicker lavas accumulated in the west (up to 1 km) than in the east (only a few hundred metres).

● How might the timing and volume of Carboniferous magmatism relate to activity in the underlying mantle?

● They suggest that there was a pulse of melting that peaked in the Early Carboniferous and then tailed off.

Figure 6.6 shows typical Early Carboniferous lava flows and vents while Figure 6.7a shows their likely extent within the SMV, in relation to major faults that were active at the time. Some of the faults may have acted as conduits for ascending magmas, as suggested by Figure 6.7b.

(a)

(b)

Figure 6.6 (a) Early Carboniferous basaltic lava flows in the western SMV, which form a prominent escarpment in the Campsie Fells, Strathclyde. The thickest flow is around 20 m thick. (b) Volcanic vents forming the prominent hills of Dumgoyne (left) and Dumfoyne (right). These vents are believed to be contemporaneous with the lavas shown in (a), being only a few kilometres away from them. (c) Tholeiitic sill near Stirling, with Stirling Castle (foreground) and the Wallace Monument (behind). The foot of the prominent line of hills is the Ochil Fault, marked close to the centre of Figure 6.8.

(c)

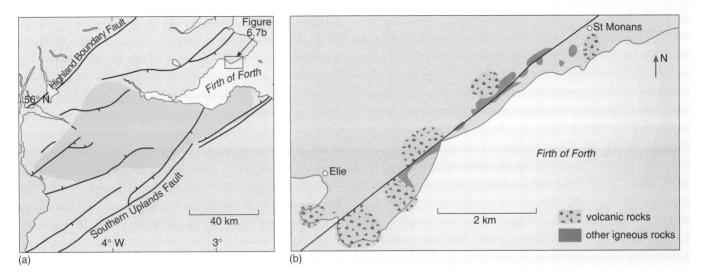

Figure 6.7   (a) Likely extent of Early Carboniferous volcanics within the Scottish Midland Valley, together with major faults which were active at the same time. The area of (b) is outlined. (b) Sketch map showing alignment of volcanic vents and associated rocks along the NE–SW Ardross Fault in Fife.

Figure 6.8 shows the orientations of dykes that were emplaced during the brief period of Late Carboniferous tholeiitic magmatism (*c.* 295 Ma, see Figure 6.5). They show an E–W orientation, in contrast to the NE–SW Caledonian trend. This brief period of magmatism, the genesis of which remains incompletely understood, also produced an extensive suite of sills, some of which form prominent landmarks throughout the SMV (Figure 6.6c). The sills have the same age and composition as the Whin Sill of northern England. The limited exposures of the SMV sills belie their more widespread extent as revealed by borehole data (Figure 6.8).

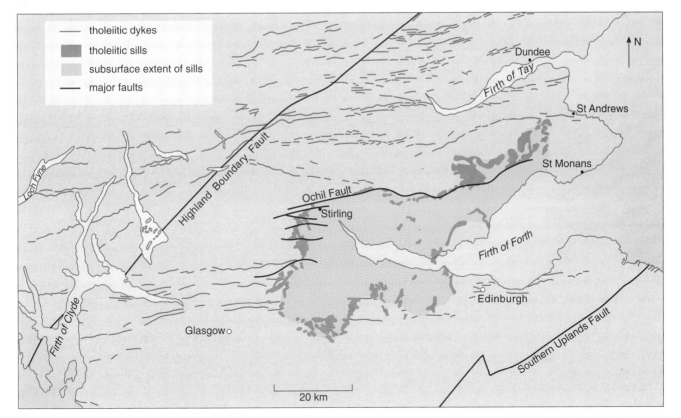

Figure 6.8   Tholeiitic Late Carboniferous E–W dyke swarm and the associated Scottish Midland Valley sill complex. The abundance of well-mapped dykes and well-known subsurface extent of the sill complex are known from coal exploration.

In the Permian (Figure 6.9), the orientation of faults and dykes across northern Europe changed again, to an almost N–S direction. Alkaline magmatism during the Permian was linked to the creation of large grabens and half-grabens, particularly the Central North Sea and around Oslo. Such Permian rifts also control the sedimentary basins of SW Scotland, the Vale of Eden and the Irish Sea.

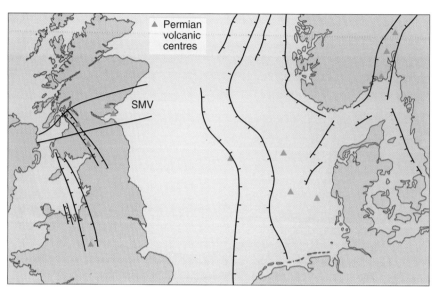

Figure 6.9   Permian rifts in north-west Europe.

⬤   What do the three different trends of dykes and rifts/grabens in the Carboniferous to Permian suggest about stresses within the lithosphere?

⬤   The dominant extensional stress field within the lithosphere changed during the Carboniferous–Permian.

6.1.2   Alkali basalt magmatism in the Early Carboniferous

Although the bulk of Early Carboniferous volcanic rocks were basaltic, more evolved rocks (e.g. phonolites, rhyolites) were produced by fractional crystallization — similar to the Icelandic central volcanoes and the Kenya Rift volcanics (Block 2, Activities 2.4 and 3.2, and Section 3.3.3). In Block 2, you saw how basalt compositions reveal information about both the thermal structure of the mantle undergoing partial melting and modifications to the magmas during their passage through the crust by crustal contamination and/or fractional crystallization. Figure 6.10 is an $Na_2O + K_2O$ vs. SiO_2 plot for the SMV volcanics and intrusions (see Block 2, Figure 2.3).

Question 6.2   In general terms, how would you classify the SMV rocks, using Figure 6.10?

As you discovered in the Kenya Rift (Block 2, Section 3.6.1), despite the SMV being an extensional environment, the dominant rock type is not tholeiitic.

Comparing the compositions of Carboniferous–Permian basalts with those from known tectonic settings is important, given the known association between Devonian magmatism and subduction (Section 5.4) 50 Ma before the beginning of the Carboniferous. Was there any lingering influence of those subduction-zone processes? Also, because the SMV developed by substantial lithospheric extension, is there a possibility that MORB-like magmas were produced, similar to those in the Red Sea (Block 2, Section 4)?

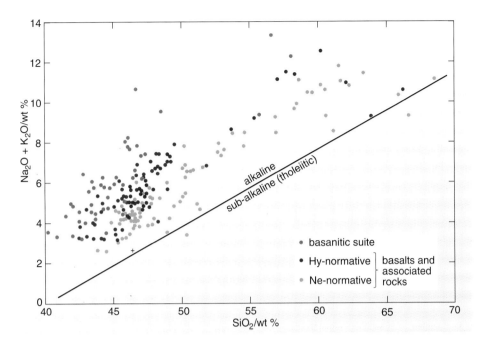

Figure 6.10 Total alkali–silica plot of Carboniferous–Permian basalts from the Scottish Midland Valley. The black line divides alkaline and subalkaline (tholeiitic) compositions.

Two lines of evidence — major elements and mantle-normalized incompatible element plots (Block 2, Activity 2.3) — are needed to investigate the affinities of basalts. Table 6.1 presents major and trace element data for a typical SMV basalt, together with a typical MORB, an OIB-continental rift alkali basalt, and a subduction zone basalt.

Table 6.1 Typical SMV basalt, and compositions of basalts from well-characterized eruptive settings (MORB, OIB-continental rift, and subduction zone). Oxides are expressed as wt %; trace elements are in ppm. LOI = loss on ignition.

	MORB	Subduction zone	OIB–continental rift	SMV basalt
SiO_2	49.21	51.31	45.68	45.36
TiO_2	1.39	0.88	2.58	1.98
Al_2O_3	15.81	18.6	14.68	12.95
FeO_t	9.12	8.42	11.36	11.74
MnO	0.16	0.15	0.17	0.24
MgO	8.53	5.95	8.92	11.80
CaO	11.14	10.30	10.44	8.05
Na_2O	2.71	2.93	3.11	2.22
K_2O	0.26	0.74	1.30	1.06
P_2O_5	0.15	0.12	0.64	0.35
LOI	–	0.30	0.73	4.46
Total	98.80	100.00	100.00	100.31
Cr	296	160	563	470
Ni	123	50	90	301
Rb	2	23	40	21
Sr	123	328	842	313
Y	43	22	25	23
Zr	100	71	213	158
Nb	4.6	2.7	84	29
Ba	12	260	600	449
Ce	11.0	29.3	96.8	43

● Based on Table 6.1, what comparisons can be drawn between the SMV alkali basalts and either the MORB or the subduction zone basalt? (Look particularly at Zr, Nb, and Ce.)

● There appears to be no close similarity between the SMV alkali basalts and the MORB or the subduction zone basalt. Trace element differences are marked, with much higher Zr, Nb, Ba, and Ce in the SMV samples.

Alkali basalts from the SMV resemble neither MORB nor subduction zone basalts. This suggests that: (i) there were no after-effects of Devonian subduction on Early Carboniferous partial melting; and (ii) rifting was not extensive enough to generate oceanic crust.

In Block 2 you met alkali basalts in the contexts of oceanic islands and continental rifts. Since the SMV formed on 40 km of older continental crust, an oceanic-island setting is not plausible! The OIB-continental rift basalt and the SMV alkali basalt have high Zr, Nb, Ba, and Ce (Table 6.1). A plot of mantle-normalized incompatible elements (Figure 6.11) shows that the SMV alkali basalts are more similar to the OIB-continental rift basalt than to either the MORB or to the subduction zone basalt. The distinctive downward trend from left to right (towards less incompatible elements) in both the SMV and the OIB–continental rift basalt indicates their enrichment in the most incompatible elements in contrast to the marked depletion in these elements in the MORB and, to a lesser extent, in the subduction-zone basalt.

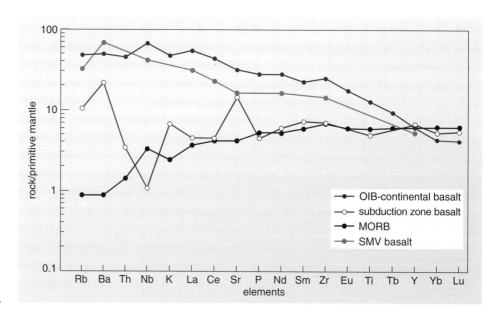

Figure 6.11 Mantle-normalized incompatible element plot, showing trends of MORB, OIB-continental rift basalt (see *Workbook 2*, Activity 2.3), a subduction zone basalt (see Block 3, Figure 3.2), and one SMV alkali basalt.

6.1.3 Alkali basalt genesis

In Block 2 (Section 3.6), you used compositions of primary basalt magmas to identify depths of melt generation and the degree of melting involved in the Kenyan lavas. Your conclusion there was that alkali basalts are typically the product of smaller melt fractions than tholeiites, and that melting occurred at greater depths (as deep as the garnet stability field if the basalt has low HREE concentrations). Early Carboniferous alkali basalts of the SMV were generated by <5% melting of mantle at the boundary between the garnet and spinel stability fields, similar to the conclusion from the study in Block 2.

An alternative approach is to look at ultramafic xenoliths and exotic crystal fragments contained within some SMV alkali basalts, as these provide direct evidence of the depth of melt generation. These xenoliths are pyroxenite together with Mg-rich garnets formed at high pressure in the mantle. Both are believed to represent a short-lived stage of partial crystallization of ascending basalt magma. Estimates from phase relationships of the temperature and pressure during this brief stopover *en route* to the surface give depths between 70 and 100 km and temperatures greater than 1300 °C. These are within the garnet stability field (Block 2, Figure 2.10), and suggest partial melting of garnet lherzolite. The presence of mantle xenoliths and crystal fragments also bears on the rate of ascent of the magma.

> **Question 6.3** If basalt magma had risen to the surface slowly, so that phase equilibrium was always maintained, what would have happened to the high-pressure pyroxenite xenoliths and garnet fragments?

Magma ascent must have been sufficiently rapid for preservation of high-pressure and high-temperature assemblages. That implies little opportunity for interaction between basalt magma and the surrounding continental crust. Although the discussion of AFC processes in Block 3 should have alerted you to the possibility of crustal contamination of basaltic magmas, extensive geochemical study of SMV basalts has revealed that it was either absent or minor.

6.1.4 Plume or no plume?

Within-plate magmatism and mantle plumes are associated in both oceanic and continental rift settings (Block 2, Sections 3 and 4). So, did a mantle plume trigger Carboniferous–Permian magmatism in the SMV?

● If plates were moving during the Carboniferous, and if a mantle plume was present, what regional feature might you expect to see?

● A hot-spot trail (Block 2, Activity 5.1).

There is no evidence anywhere in NW Europe for a hot-spot trail associated with magmatism of this age, but this is not conclusive evidence against a plume. Hot-spot trails are not ubiquitous features of mantle plume activity; for instance, no hot-spot trail relates to the separation of Australia and Antarctica.

● How does the lithosphere respond to the arrival of a mantle plume?

● Doming typically accompanies mantle plumes impacting beneath continental lithosphere. For example, the NE African lithosphere domed in response to the Afar plume, followed by subsidence and sedimentation (Block 2).

The pattern of sedimentation in the SMV records widespread and continued subsidence during basaltic magmatism, with no sign of doming. There is no evidence in the SMV, from either a hot-spot trail or from doming-related erosion and sedimentation, to support the presence of a plume as the source of the volcanism. Not all continental rift systems are the same.

6.1.5 Passive and active rifting

Rift systems can be classified into active and passive types, depending on the relative timing of doming and erosion, sedimentation, thermal subsidence, and rift-related igneous rocks. **Active rifts** are initiated by processes in the mantle *below* the lithosphere, usually mantle plumes, and are characterized by early lithospheric doming in response to the additional buoyancy provided by heat from the plume. Once the lithosphere has thinned, either by extension or rapid erosion, relatively large volumes of volcanic rocks are erupted. Subsidence and renewed sedimentation are the response to cooling of the plume, or to thinned lithosphere moving away from it. In contrast, **passive rifts** are caused by stresses *within* the lithosphere, which is stretched and thinned by plate forces. The earliest expression of rifting is then subsidence and sedimentation. A passive rift is therefore characterized by the production of substantial thicknesses of sedimentary rocks (with or without minor volumes of volcanics).

Thinning and stretching of the lithosphere beneath a passive rift can induce underlying mantle to rise, thereby encouraging decompression melting at relatively shallow depths. Thus, a passive rift can evolve into an active rift. The converse can occur with an active rift. If a mantle plume is weak and unable to sustain prolonged magmatism, an active rift can evolve into a passive rift, provided that lithospheric stresses favour continued but modest extension. Figure 6.12 summarizes the key features of passive and active rifts.

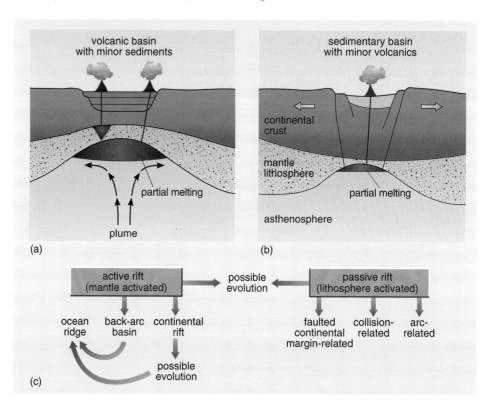

Figure 6.12 (a) Diagrammatic cross-section of an active rift. (b) Diagrammatic cross-section of a passive rift. (c) Potential evolutionary paths of active rifts and passive rifts.

Here are the key features of the SMV magmatism, in relation to active versus passive rift models:

1 there is no evidence for doming of the lithosphere;

2 sediment thickness (4 km) is far greater than that of volcanics (<1 km in the west to a few hundred metres in the east);

3 subsidence along normal faults occurred throughout the volcanism;

4 a β factor of 1.4 indicates lithospheric extension, but not complete failure of the lithosphere;

5 there is no hot-spot trail;

6 magmatic activity lasted from the Early Carboniferous to Early Permian, a period of 80 Ma; it began with alkali basalts, followed by tholeiitic basalts later in the Carboniferous, and returned to alkali basalts in the Permian.

The small volume of magma, together with the absence of regional doming, does not support active rifting. The episodic nature of magmatism — from alkaline to tholeiitic to alkaline — over about 80 Ma points towards an important and long-lived role for the lithosphere. Fluctuating compositions may reflect changing extensional stress within the lithosphere. SMV magmatism was probably induced during passive rifting that allowed the mantle to rise, decompress, and partially melt. The mantle barely managed to melt at all, giving only small degrees of partial melting to form alkaline magmas.

6.1.6   The SMV in a NW European context

The SMV is the result of larger-scale processes that took place across NW Europe during the Carboniferous–Permian. Figure 6.9 shows a system of large, sediment-dominated rifts that formed during the Permian, some of which include contemporary volcanic and intrusive igneous rocks. The rifts indicate regional E–W extension of continental lithosphere that had amalgamated before the start of the Devonian. The SMV rift bucks this trend, and was a response to extensional forces during the Carboniferous, which emphasized Caledonian terrane boundaries. Permian rifting cut completely across this basement architecture. The site of Permian extensional activity lay to the north of the Variscan Front, where yet more crustal masses were in the process of accretion to what would become northern Pangaea (Figure 5.20). This culminated in the Variscan Orogeny with the collision between Laurasia and Gondwana, to form a roughly equatorial mountain range rivalling the modern Himalaya. Crustal shortening spanned the Carboniferous and Early Permian, a setting hardly conducive to plume-related continental break-up. The SMV formed in the foreland of these Variscan orogenic events. The evidence that you have considered points strongly towards passive rifting. Precisely how this arose is the subject of continued research across the whole area of Figure 6.9.

6.1.7   Summary of Section 6.1

- The Scottish Midland Valley (SMV) developed during the Devonian and Carboniferous Periods, whilst Pangaea was consolidating.

- Extensional tectonics produced a graben-like structure, within which substantial thicknesses of sediments accumulated.

- Carboniferous sedimentation indicates that periodic marine incursions affected the SMV.

- The SMV crust comprises some 40 km of compositionally diverse rocks.

- A pulse of alkali basalt magmatism began (and peaked) during the Early Carboniferous, and continued through towards the end of the Carboniferous. This pulse of magmatism was associated with extensional re-activation of older Caledonian (NE–SW and ENE–WSW) structures.

- A short-lived pulse of tholeiitic magmatism, associated with N–S extension in the Late Carboniferous, is overprinted onto the declining alkali basalt magmatism initiated in the Early Carboniferous.

- In the Early Permian, a new pulse of alkali basalt magmatism was initiated, associated with roughly E–W extension.

- The SMV alkali basalts show no influence of Late Silurian subduction some 50 Ma earlier.

- Compositions of SMV basalts indicate that stretching and thinning of the lithosphere was insufficient to generate MORB.

- The SMV alkali basalts have close affinities with OIB–continental rift alkali basalts.

- There is no conclusive evidence for the existence of one or more mantle plumes triggering the production of the SMV alkali basalts.

- Using the classification of rifts into active and passive, the SMV would be classed as a passive rift.

- The mantle beneath the SMV barely melted, which explains the dominance of alkali basalts (via small degrees of partial melting), and the relatively small volumes of igneous rocks relative to sedimentary rocks in the SMV.

6.2 The British Tertiary Igneous Province

We complete this Block by considering the youngest and most spectacular igneous event to impact on the continental lithosphere of the British Isles — the **British Tertiary Igneous Province** (BTIP), which forms part of the larger North Atlantic Tertiary **Igneous** Province (NATP). Historically, the BTIP has been an important area for the development of ideas about the generation of lava series and the initiation of mantle plumes and continental break-up, and continues to be so. We focus on:

1 the timing and duration of volcanism;

2 the geochemistry of the magmatism and how it relates to the thermal state and composition of mantle plumes;

3 the role that the lithosphere and crust have in controlling and modifying the chemical composition of magmas;

4 the evolution of the mantle plume over the last 63 Ma and of sea-floor spreading in the North Atlantic.

The NATP extends from NE Canada through Greenland, Iceland, Jan Mayen and the Faeroes to the NW British Isles (Figure 6.13), and during its initial stages

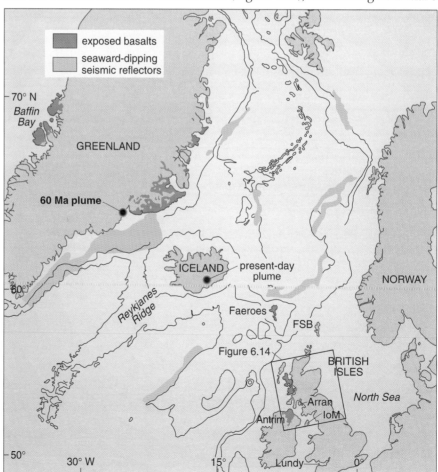

Figure 6.13 Map of the North Atlantic Tertiary Province, showing bathymetry (500 m and 2000 m contours) of the present North Atlantic and the locations of the ancestral Iceland plume (at 60 Ma) and its present position. FSB = Faeroe–Shetland Basin. The inset shows the location of Figure 6.14.

it spanned an area at least 2000 km wide. Many NATP igneous centres were controlled by earlier structures in the lithosphere. Mesozoic extension had formed sedimentary basins in NW Britain, and the BTIP volcanic centres are located over locally thinned lithosphere. The lavas found in Canada, Greenland, the Faeroes, Scotland and Northern Ireland were all erupted during early Tertiary times (63–58 Ma). The volcanically active oceanic islands of Iceland and Jan Mayen formed in more recent times. As you found in Block 2 (Activity 2.4 and Section 5.2), the mantle plume that generated the extensive NATP flood basalts during the Tertiary is the source for modern volcanism in Iceland; the Iceland mantle plume has been active for 63 Ma. During this period, the style of NATP volcanism has changed from continental flood basalts, through break-up of the North Atlantic continent, to the current intersection of the mid-Atlantic Ridge with the plume in Iceland itself. Although we will concentrate on magmatism in the BTIP, we shall return to the evolution of the Iceland plume over the last 63 million years.

Figure 6.14 shows details of the BTIP, specifically the extensive outcrops of igneous rocks in the Hebrides, the mainland of western Scotland and Northern Ireland.

● Briefly describe the form and distribution of the magmatism in the BTIP.

● There are extensive lava fields, particularly in the Western Isles of Scotland and County Antrim, and several plutonic centres. Major dyke swarms extend from the plutonic centres across much of western Scotland and into northern England and Northern Ireland.

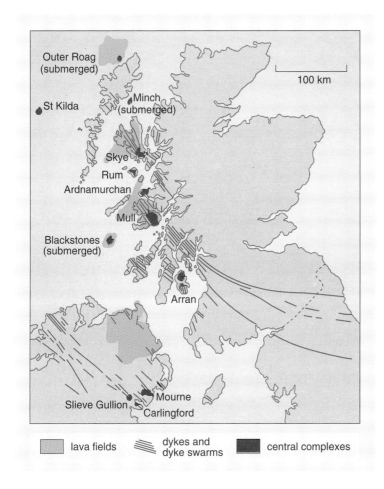

lava fields   dykes and dyke swarms   central complexes

Figure 6.14 Igneous features of the BTIP.

The volcanic occurrences consist of basaltic lava flows, originally up to 2 km thick, often with a central intrusive complex. These flows erupted from fissures located around the central volcanoes (Block 2, Activity 2.4). There are differences in the rocks exposed from area to area. The islands of Skye, Mull and Rum, which occur in the Hebridean Terrane, are the focus of your investigations. The thickest sequences of lavas occur on Skye and Mull. On Skye, plateau-type lavas (Figure 6.15) are termed the Skye Main Lava Series (SMLS), and consist of primitive basalts with rare, more evolved compositions such as trachytes. Overlying these are more restricted lavas, which include the MORB-like basalts of the Preshal More Group. Skye also exposes spectacular intrusive rocks. The Cuillin gabbros are younger than the SMLS and have chemical affinities with the Preshal More sequence. Two groups of granites, the Western Red Hills and the Eastern Red Hills, record progressively later magmatism. Finally, late-stage dykes represent the youngest igneous rocks on Skye.

Thick basaltic lavas (1700 m) are also exposed on Mull. The lowest lavas comprise the Mull Plateau Group (MPG), which is equivalent to the SMLS. Above these are the Coire Gorm (CG) lavas and Central Mull Tholeiites (CMT), the latter being the equivalent to the Preshal More group.

The island of Rum is made up of dominantly ultramafic and mafic cumulate rocks termed the Rum Layered Igneous Complex. These are the remnants of an old magma chamber formerly beneath a central volcano that has been exposed by erosion.

The BTIP exhibits several magmatic events — early thick sequences of plateau-type magmatism are followed by localized lavas. The granites of Skye, Rum and Arran, the dyke swarms, and some silica-rich volcanics represent the final phase of magmatism.

Figure 6.15 View of Skye Main Lava Series, Duirnish, north-west Skye.

6.2.1   Timing and duration of magmatism

High-precision Ar–Ar dating of the main lava series, together with U–Pb zircon ages of some of the more fractionated rocks of the intrusive complexes (Figure 6.16), has replaced earlier results, whose precision could not resolve the many events in the BTIP.

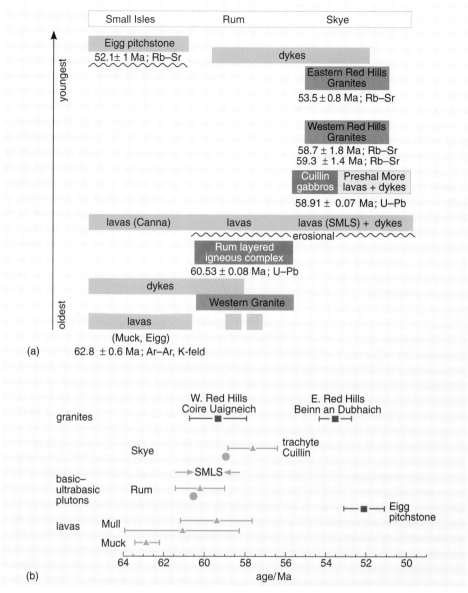

(a)

(b)

Figure 6.16 (a) Simplified igneous stratigraphy of Skye, Rum and the Small Isles (Muck and Eigg) based on field relationships and best available radiometric ages. (b) Radiometric ages and error bars for different igneous activity in the BTIP.

The oldest lava flow in the BTIP (62.8 ± 0.6 Ma) occurs on the islands of Muck and Eigg, and was erupted at the same time as the Iceland plume impacted on the lithosphere across the North Atlantic region. A 60.53 ± 0.08 Ma U–Pb zircon age for a peridotite in the Rum Layered Igneous Complex indicates that the Rum intrusion must have formed before eruption of the main plateau-type basalts on Mull and Skye. It was also uplifted and eroded, because clasts of the intrusion occur in sediments interbedded with the lower flows of the Skye Main Lava Series. The SMLS is hydrothermally altered and imprecisely dated. Pegmatites in the Cuillin gabbros have yielded a U–Pb zircon age of 58.91 ± 0.07 Ma. Because the Cuillin gabbros are younger than the SMLS, these two very precise dates show that the SMLS was erupted in a maximum period of 1.6 Ma. The base of the less altered Mull Plateau Group has an Ar–Ar age of 60.5 ± 0.5 and its top gives 58.38 ± 0.19 Ma, suggesting a maximum eruption time on Mull of just over 2 Ma. Similar dates characterize the West Greenland plateau-type basalts, so the initial flood-basalts in the NATP erupted over a very short time period (1.5–2.5 Ma), as did those of many other continental flood basalt provinces. This may be a feature of the impact of plume heads with the base of the lithosphere (Block 2, Section 5.3).

The Cuillin gabbros' U–Pb age of 58.91 ± 0.07 Ma also probably dates the Preshal More lavas and dykes, to which they are chemically similar, and is slightly older than the youngest Mull lavas. Less precise Rb–Sr ages for the Western Red Hill granites (59.3 ± 1.4 and 58.7 ± 1.8 Ma) cannot be distinguished from that of the Cuillin gabbro. Granites of the Eastern Red Hills are younger (Rb–Sr age of 53.5 ± 0.8 Ma). The youngest rock dated in the BTIP is a flow of high-SiO_2 glassy lava on the island of Eigg (Rb–Sr age of 52.1 ± 1.0 Ma). So the whole BTIP formed over only about 10 Ma.

6.2.2 Lava geochemistry

Circulation of hot fluids during intrusion of the central complexes altered the lava sequences in the BTIP extensively, thereby changing their chemistry and making dating difficult. Nonetheless, there is a huge amount of geochemical data for the BTIP from unaltered centres of flows and away from obvious fluid pathways. Rather than cover all the volcanic occurrences, we focus on lavas from the island of Mull (Table 6.2). Figure 6.17 plots the variation of CaO, Na_2O and Mg# against MgO for the three main lava types on Mull. Plots of the Skye data look very similar.

> Question 6.4 (a) Describe the differences between the three Mull lava groups, in terms of CaO, Na_2O and MgO contents. (b) Could any of the lavas from the three groups have been in equilibrium with mantle olivine?

Combined petrographic and geochemical studies suggest that primary melts on Mull have MgO contents of 15–16% (basalts with MgO >16% probably involved olivine accumulation). These primary lavas also have SiO_2 contents less than 46%.

> Question 6.5 Using Figure 2.17 in Block 2 and the information given above, estimate the pressure and temperature of formation of the primary Mull basalts.

Basalts with such high MgO contents formed in equilibrium with mantle olivine, and had high eruption temperatures. The most primitive plateau basalts on Mull are often nepheline-normative, and also have high iron contents. Their geochemistry as a whole suggests melt generation at high mantle temperatures and pressures, and modelling of the major elements indicates mantle potential temperatures of 1480 °C (200 °C above that of the ambient mantle) at depths greater than 80 km. The most likely explanation of such high mantle temperatures is a mantle plume. High-MgO lavas are widespread in the NATP,

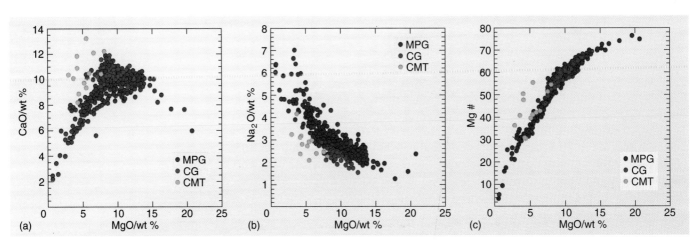

Figure 6.17 Plots of (a) CaO (wt %), (b) Na_2O (wt %) and (c) Mg# as a function of MgO contents for the MPG, CG and CMT lava groups on Mull. Mg# is calculated as described in Block 2. (Data from A.C. Kerr.)

Table 6.2 Geochemical analyses of four lavas and three silica-rich Lewisian gneisses from Mull and Tiree. Oxides are expressed as wt %; trace elements in ppm. The ratios that involve REE are normalized to C1 chondrite data and the Ba/Nb ratio to primitive mantle values. CG Coire Gorm; MPG Mull Plateau Group; CMT Central Mull Tholeiites.

Sample	BR8	BR1	BM85	CA15	P42	P43	P50
Type	MPG	MPG	CG	CMT	Leucogneiss	Leucogneiss	Leucogneiss
SiO_2	46.79	45.39	45.90	47.94	69.71	72.07	72.89
TiO_2	1.22	2.55	1.38	1.07	0.29	0.18	0.09
Al_2O_3	13.39	15.83	16.59	15.29	14.39	14.25	14.15
Fe_2O_3(tot)	12.33	16.32	12.78	12.49	2.33	1.70	0.65
MnO	0.17	0.20	0.17	0.20	0.02	0.00	0.00
MgO	13.49	6.95	10.88	8.09	1.10	0.59	0.50
CaO	9.64	7.67	10.51	12.17	2.09	0.86	0.75
Na_2O	2.42	3.76	2.08	2.22	4.98	3.21	2.84
K_2O	0.43	0.24	0.23	0.05	4.20	5.40	6.81
P_2O_5	0.16	0.26	0.12	0.09	0.13	0.09	0.03
LOI	1.46	2.62	–	–	0.50	0.43	0.43
Total	100.04	99.17	100.64	99.61	99.24	98.35	98.71
Mg#	0.71	0.48	0.65	0.59	0.51	0.43	0.63
Sc	30	18	29.4	40.6	5	4	2
V	217	270	244	303	35	28	13
Cr	991	149	433	283	22	18	17
Ni	350	99	312	106	19	5	8
Rb	6	3	4.9	3	101	72	125
Sr	304	374	167	123	541	822	565
Y	18	25	24.8	31.3	5	1	1
Zr	90	161	73	63	98	63	14
Nb	5.2	8	6.5	5.6	4	2	2
Ba	252	61	107	47	1388	6881	3825
La	6.83	6.58	4.89	3.29	38.17	6.31	9.02
Ce	16.87	18.68	11.49	8.2	74.48	8.2	10.28
Pr	2.56	3.14	1.61	1.27	6.62	0.9	0.86
Nd	12.01	16.84	9.8	6.12	23.08	3.48	2.78
Sm	3.27	5.17	3.39	2.83	3.94	1.08	0.81
Eu	1.13	1.88	1.45	1.2	1.29	3.2	1.95
Gd	3.61	5.57	4.28	3.95	3.03	1.16	0.95
Tb	0.59	0.87	0.71	0.68	0.23	0.1	0.09
Dy	3.36	4.77	5.1	4.62	1.03	0.5	0.49
Ho	0.66	0.9	1.1	0.95	0.15	0.11	0.12
Er	1.77	2.41	2.92	2.92	0.42	0.31	0.41
Tm	0.28	0.32	0.49	0.4	0.05	0.05	0.08
Yb	1.65	2.05	2.84	2.9	0.35	0.47	0.55
Lu	0.23	0.3	0.4	0.38	0.05	0.05	0.06
Pb	1.61	1.11	0.79	1.44	13.49	9.39	14.07
Th	0.22	0.55	0.66	0.31	3.99	0.9	0.86
U	0.07	0.16	–	–	0.26	0.07	0.12
$[Ba/Nb]_N$	4.94	0.78	1.68	0.86	35.4	351	195
$[La/Yb]_N$	2.97	2.30	1.24	0.81	78.2	9.63	11.8
$[La/Nd]_N$	1.12	0.77	0.98	1.06	3.26	3.57	6.39
$[Dy/Yb]_N$	1.36	1.56	1.20	1.07	1.97	0.71	0.60

and seem to have been erupted around the same time everywhere (just after 63 Ma). This has led most workers to suggest that a mantle plume head impacted on the lithosphere about 63 million years ago (Block 2, Section 5.3), to produce large volumes of primitive magma, perhaps covering an area 2000 km across. So, the BTIP formed differently from the Carboniferous SMV volcanic rocks, as a result of mantle-activated processes rather than passive rifting.

Figure 6.17 shows other features in the BTIP that bear on changes in melt geochemistry over time. The MPG and CG lavas are similar, but the most primitive CG lavas have slightly higher SiO_2 contents (not shown) and distinctly lower Na_2O contents. The higher silica in the CG suggests that their melting occurred at slightly lower pressures than for the MPG, whereas the lower sodium contents of the CG suggest higher degrees of partial melting. Although there are no primitive CMT lavas, their geochemistry suggests higher degrees of melting at even lower pressures (<2 GPa). Overall, there seems to have been a decrease in the depth of melting during the evolution of the BTIP, but increasing degrees of partial melting. We will discuss this point in more detail later. Data from experimental studies of basalt crystallization at different pressures suggest that the SMLS and MPG lavas fractionally crystallized at a depth of ~27 km, but the Preshal More (and by inference CMT) lavas fractionated at depths of less than 1 km. This suggests that the early plateau lavas ponded at the base of the crust, whereas the Preshal More and CMT lavas underwent fractionation very close to the surface, perhaps just beneath the volcanoes.

Trace element characteristics of the Mull lavas add interesting details to this gross petrogenetic picture. Figure 6.18 shows REE plots for the four lavas and three quartz- and feldspar-rich Lewisian gneisses from Table 6.2.

⬤ Describe the essential characteristics of the REE patterns (Figure 6.18, Table 6.2) for each of the lavas and the leucogneisses.

⬤ BR1 has a smooth LREE-enriched pattern with low HREE contents. BR8 has a similar REE pattern but is less LREE-enriched and in fact has $[La/Nd]_N$ ratios less than one. BM 85 has a rather flat REE pattern (with slightly elevated La and Ce) and higher HREE contents than the previous two lavas. CA15 has a slightly LREE-depleted pattern ($[La/Yb]_N$ ratios less than one). All the gneisses have LREE-enriched patterns with very low HREE contents, and two (P43, P50) show large positive Eu anomalies (see Block 3).

The significance of the Lewisian gneisses will become clear shortly, because they are believed to have played a role in the petrogenesis of the Mull lavas. The next step is to look at the REE patterns of the basalts, in terms of mantle melting. LREE-enriched patterns in basalts generally indicate a small amount of melting.

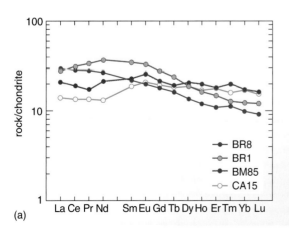
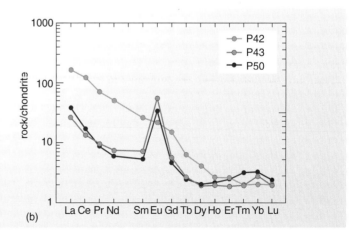

Figure 6.18 Chondrite-normalized REE plots of (a) four representative Mull basalts covering the three lava groups described in the text and (b) three Lewisian granulite-facies leucogneisses from Mull and Tiree. Analyses can be found in Table 6.2.

The low HREE relative to LREE of BR8 and BR1 (MPG examples), and their high [La/Yb]$_N$ ratios, are characteristic of melting in the garnet–peridotite field. This tallies with major element evidence for small amounts of partial melting at great depth and high temperatures. BM85 (CG) has a rather flatter REE pattern without such elevated [La/Yb]$_N$ ratios, suggesting higher degrees of melting in both the garnet–peridotite and spinel–peridotite field. Finally, CA15 (MPG) has a flat MREE-HREE pattern and is LREE-depleted. Such a pattern can be modelled only by high degrees of melting in the spinel–peridotite field. Figure 6.19 summarizes the differences in REE patterns of the three Mull lava types by plotting the ratio of a middle- to heavy-REE ratio ([Dy/Yb]$_N$) to that of a light- to heavy-REE ratio ([La/Yb]$_N$).

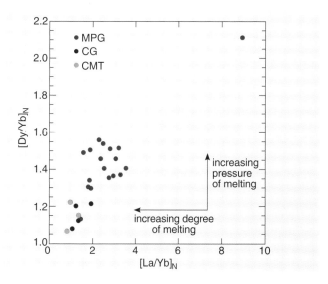

Figure 6.19 Plots of [Dy/Yb]$_N$ versus [La/Yb]$_N$ for the Mull lava groups. The vectors illustrate the effects of increasing the degree of partial melting, which lowers the [La/Yb]$_N$ ratio, and increasing the pressure of melting into the garnet–peridotite field, which increases the [Dy/Yb]$_N$ ratio.

What do the REE patterns in Figure 6.18 and the data in Figure 6.19 signify, in terms of the thickness of the lithosphere, as magmatism progressed from the MPG to the CMT?

The data indicate that MPG lavas were generated by the lowest degree of partial melting and the highest pressure of melting (estimated to be <5% melting at >2.5 GPa). In contrast, both the CG and CMT lava groups represent higher melt fractions and were generated by melting at lower pressures (estimated to be 5–13% melting for the CG lavas and >13% melting for the CMT lavas, at pressures less than 2.5 GPa).

Although higher mantle potential temperatures should produce higher melt fractions than from ambient mantle (Block 2, Section 2.4.3), this is only true if the mantle can melt all the way to the Earth's surface. Thick lithosphere restricts the amount of decompression melting. Melting during the initial stages of BTIP magmatism started very deep with a garnet–peridotite source, but was restricted by thick lithosphere to producing low melt fractions of Ne-normative alkaline magma. Through time, the initial depth of melting decreased, the melt fraction increased and the final pressure of melting decreased. The CMT lavas were generated by extensive amounts of melting of spinel peridotite at shallow pressures. One inference is that the lithosphere thinned from the time of eruption of the MPG to that of the CMT lavas. Modelling of the REE data suggests that 30 km of lithosphere was removed during the evolution of the BTIP lavas over only 2–2.5 Ma, probably by a combination of thermal erosion and extension.

6.2.3 The role of crustal contamination

The fact that BTIP magmas had to penetrate thick continental lithosphere, combined with evidence for lithospheric thinning, suggests that crustal contamination may have played a role in magmagenesis.

- What crustal rock types are likely to be beneath the BTIP volcanics?

- The bulk of the crust of the Hebridean Terrane is Lewisian gneiss, overlain by thick Torridonian sandstones and thin Cambro-Ordovician marine sediments.

When basaltic magma moves through the crust, it has the potential to assimilate crustal material, largely because the solidus for silica-rich crustal rocks is at lower temperatures than that of basaltic magma. The processes involved in assimilation depend on several factors: the time taken by magma to traverse the crust; composition of the crust; geometry and size of the magma conduit; and whether the lava is fractionating (Block 3, Section 4.4.2).

Assimilated crustal material changes the major, trace-element and isotopic 'signatures' of a magma. If the magma moves through the crust rapidly, then there may be little chance of assimilating crustal rocks (but see below). If magma moves slowly, perhaps ponding in a fractionating magma chamber, it is more able to incorporate large amounts of crust, by the assimilation and fractional crystallization (AFC) process (Block 3, Section 4.4). The isotopic composition of many evolved continental lava series can be explained by AFC processes. However, hot, primitive magma is generally very fluid, and probably travels to the surface by turbulent flow. If the magma conduits have a large surface area, then primitive melts may assimilate large amounts of crustal material, by a process called assimilation during turbulent ascent (ATA). Figure 6.20 shows data that can be used to assess whether AFC or ATA processes might have influenced the composition of the Mull MPG lavas.

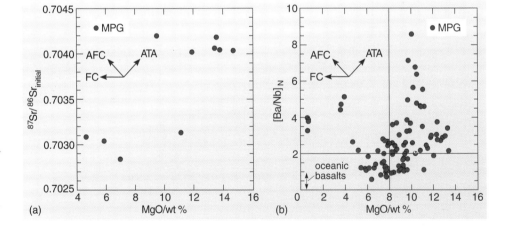

Figure 6.20 Plots of: (a) initial $^{87}Sr/^{86}Sr$ ratio; (b) $[Ba/Nb]_N$ ratio versus MgO for the MPG lavas. Marked on the plots are vectors illustrating the effects of fractional crystallization (FC), assimilation and fractional crystallization (AFC) and assimilation during turbulent ascent (ATA).

Question 6.6 Figure 6.20a is a plot of initial $^{87}Sr/^{86}Sr$ ratio versus MgO for the MPG lavas. Which type of contamination process may have occurred and why?

Figure 6.20b shows that the most isotopically contaminated lavas also have the highest $[Ba/Nb]_N$ ratios, which implies that the local crust also has a high $[Ba/Nb]_N$ ratio.

During the initiation of magmatism in the BTIP, the first melts would have had to generate the conduits through which they travelled. This suggests considerable interaction between magma and crust. Theoretical calculations indicate that a conduit >3 m wide would produce turbulent flow for the primitive BTIP lavas and that a conduit 3–4 m wide would produce the maximum turbulent flow with the greatest amount of interaction and assimilation.

In Block 2, you studied mantle-normalized multi-element plots of average OIB and MORB as well as those from Ethiopian basalts. Partial melting of the mantle and fractional crystallization of basaltic magmas generally produces relatively smooth-patterned plots. Figure 6.21 shows such plots for the same Mull lavas and Lewisian samples as in Figure 6.18. The patterns of the lavas are 'spiky' rather than smooth as expected for products of just partial melting alone. Sample BR8 has strong enrichment in Ba, and depletion in Th and Nb, a characteristic feature of all lavas with high $[BA/Nb]_N$ rations (Figure 6.20). Lava BR1 has a smoother pattern, BM85 has a flat pattern with slight enrichment in Ba, and CA15 is slightly depleted in the most incompatible elements and shows strong K depletion. The gneisses are enriched in the most incompatible elements, with very high Ba, K and Sr contents, and strongly depleted in Nb and Th.

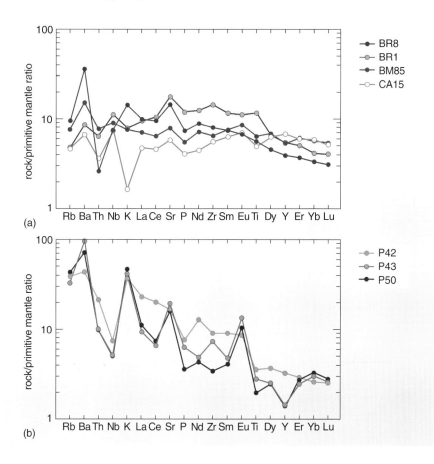

(a)

(b)

Figure 6.21 Mantle-normalized plots of: (a) four representative Mull basalts covering the three lava groups described in the text; (b) three Lewisian granulite-facies leucogneisses from Mull and Tiree. Analyses can be found in Table 6.2.

Anomalously high Ba and K contents are common features of many primitive BTIP lavas and suggests that the crustal contaminant is also K-rich. If the lavas were contaminated by Lewisian gneisses like those illustrated, that would explain the lavas' high K contents and elevated $[Ba/Nb]_N$ ratios. The LREE-enriched nature of some of the lavas might also have arisen from assimilation of such crustal material. BR1 is not contaminated at all, whereas the increase in the $[La/Nd]_N$ ratio of BR8 reflects contamination by crustal rocks.

Establishing whether the BTIP lavas have assimilated either upper or lower crust would provide evidence for the depths involved in the lavas' evolution. Geochemists who work on the BTIP assume that amphibolite-facies Lewisian gneisses represent the middle crust of the Hebridean Terrane and granulite-facies Lewisian represents the lower crust. Torridonian sandstones probably represent the upper crust. Using a combination of Sr and Pb isotopes helps to untangle which parts of the crust have contaminated the BTIP lavas. Lewisian granulite-facies rocks have distinctive Pb and Sr isotope characteristics because they are unusually depleted in their parent elements (Rb, and Th and U respectively). The Sr and Pb isotopes in MPG basalts indicate that little if any middle crust was involved in their contamination. In fact, the isotope data suggest that any contamination was by the easily melted Lewisian granulite-facies leucogneisses such as those described in this Section. This suggests that the primitive BTIP magmas stagnated and then made their way through the lower crust, assimilating crust as they moved turbulently upwards, which matches evidence that the SMLS and MPG lavas fractionally crystallized at ~27 km depth (Section 6.2.2).

The widespread association of granite intrusions with the BTIP basaltic magmatism has intrigued geologists for more than half a century. There have been two main hypotheses for their formation: as a result of extreme fractionation of the BTIP parent magmas; or by localized crustal melting. The granites were emplaced during the less voluminous stages of volcanism — the Preshal More and CG phases of the Skye and Mull centres. The Sr and Pb isotopes in the granites are dominated by middle or upper crustal signatures. Although some of the granites could be explained by extreme contamination of the basaltic lavas coupled with fractional crystallization, this is not a likely explanation for the large volume of granitic material that was generated. In Section 6.2.2, you saw that the youngest of the BTIP lavas underwent fractional crystallization at very shallow levels in the crust. Heating of the country rock around a magma chamber at 1200 °C could have caused considerable melting of the plentiful granitic material, either from amphibolite-grade Lewisian crust (Activity 4.1) or the quartz- and feldspar-rich Torridonian sandstones.

6.2.4 Magmatism and continental break-up: the Iceland plume

Continental break-up in the NATP is best recorded by drilling and seismic studies off the SE coast of Greenland. During the initial development of the NATP there was significant crustal underplating by basaltic magma, as well as volcanism. The underplating produced 10–30 km of mafic crust that shows as prominent seismic reflectors (pale green on Figure 6.13) between these depths. Dating of drilled examples of these reflectors provides evidence that the North Atlantic remnant of Pangaea began to break up at ~55 Ma. Geochemical studies show that the amount of crustal contamination decreases in magmas younger than 55 Ma, as the North Atlantic began to open and became oceanic in character. The Faeroes–Iceland ridge (Figure 6.13) tracks the evolution of the Iceland plume and its magmatic products from the time of break-up to the present day. Although the current tectonic setting of Iceland is different from that of the NATP, major and trace element and isotopic studies indicate that there are many similarities in the mantle plume sources tapped by the Iceland plume over the last 63 Ma.

6.2.5 Summary of Section 6.2

- Volcanism in the NATP began at 63 Ma with the impact of the Iceland plume on the North Atlantic remnant of Pangaea. Large volumes of hot primitive magmas were rapidly erupted between 61–59 Ma.

- The main plateau basalts are Ne-normative, magnesian lavas, which melted at elevated temperatures in the garnet–peridotite field, in a mantle plume. They fractionated at the base of the crust.

- Melting that produced basalts over 2 Ma later indicates that the lithosphere progressively thinned by up to 30 km beneath the main volcanic centres, either by extension or thermal erosion.

- Many of the early primitive lavas show signs of crustal contamination, but the later more evolved lavas do not. Contamination was due to a process of assimilation during turbulent ascent. Isotopes indicate that in the BTIP Lewisian deep crustal materials were the most common contaminant.

- Granite intrusions and acid volcanics dominate the later stages of magmatism in the BTIP. These represent melting of the crust in association with fractionation of basaltic magmas in the upper crust.

- At ~55 Ma, the North Atlantic began to open. The Faeroes–Iceland ridge tracks the evolution of the Iceland plume to the present day. Lavas on Iceland are geochemically similar to those of the Tertiary NATP. This indicates that the Iceland plume has been tapping the same mantle source material over 63 Ma.

Objectives for Section 6

Now you have completed this Section, you should be able to:

6.1   Understand the meaning of all the terms printed in **bold**.

6.2   Describe the relationship between crustal structures and associated basaltic magmatism.

6.3   Compare and contrast basalt compositions to evaluate the source and extent of mantle partial melting and crustal contamination.

6.4   Classify rifts as either passive or active.

Question 6.7   What are the main differences between the tectonic settings of volcanic rocks in the SMV and the BTIP?

Question 6.8   What is the main reason *not* to suspect an influence by crustal contamination in the SMV basalts?

7 Concluding remarks

The history of geological discovery has increasingly depended on applying what is known from one continent to the geology of another. For example, understanding subduction and terrane accretion in northern Britain during the Late Precambrian and Early Paleozoic was only possible after the tectonic evolution of the eastern seaboard of North America had been worked out from more revealing and extensive exposures there. But this process of moving from the more obvious to the more obscure has not been entirely one-way. Fortunately for us, the astonishing variety of geology that can be found in the British Isles, and the challenges presented by our own geological record, have spurred many developments both in theory and in methods of gathering data. For example, advances in metamorphic and structural geology made by geologists working on rocks of the Scottish Highlands from the late 19th century to the present, provided the techniques for deciphering the tectonics of more modern mountain ranges such as the Alps and the Himalaya. That in turn triggered a much better understanding of the Caledonian orogeny.

Another example is how the first igneous petrologists in the early part of the 20th century laid down the fundamental basis for understanding effusive and plutonic magmatism from their studies of lavas and granitic intrusions in the BTIP and the Devonian and Carboniferous igneous centres of the British Isles. Despite the small areas of exposed rocks, they are unique in having been studied continually for over 150 years. As you have seen, they still provide deep insights into how continental lithosphere has evolved over the last 3000 Ma.

You have now reached the end not only of the Block but also of this Course. At the beginning of Block 1, we emphasized that the evidence for how our home planet has evolved is mainly preserved on the continents. Armed with this evidence and with the knowledge of what it represents, your travels over the continents, whether near to home or abroad, will be enriched.

Answers and comments to Questions

Question 2.1 The Permo-Triassic basin is related to a small, negative Bouguer anomaly. Where the strata dip off the Carboniferous rocks to the west the slope of the anomaly is gentle, but where the basin is bounded to the east by the Pennine Fault there is a sharp gravity feature that parallels it. The negative anomaly is probably caused by thick, low-density Permo-Trias sediments that are poorly cemented. The immediately underlying Carboniferous strata are dominated by compact and higher density limestones.

Question 2.2 The Alston and Askrigg Blocks are believed to lie above two large granite plutons — the Weardale and Wensleydale granites respectively. Broad negative anomalies are associated with the two blocks, separated by a 'ridge' running W–E (also a negative Bouguer anomaly, but higher than those either side of it). The other granite of which you should be aware is that beneath the southern Lake District. This coincides with a negative anomaly that has deep features associated with the outcropping granites (Skiddaw in particular). Other broad negative lows occur beneath the Cheviot Hills, Criffel and Cairnsmore of Fleet granites in the Borders. Although they look the same, lows over the Solway Firth and eastern Irish Sea relate to broad Permo-Triassic basins.

Question 2.3 The Cairnsmore of Fleet, Criffel and Cheviot granites in the Borders show as annular or 'doughnut'-shaped magnetic anomalies. These are not due to the granites themselves, but to the growth of magnetic minerals in their contact-metamorphic aureoles, thereby explaining their annular shape. The small outcrops of granite in the western Lake District show as a cluster of small anomalies. The Shap granite, despite its small outcrop, shows as a prominent positive anomaly. The large, buried granite masses indicated by negative Bouguer anomalies beneath the Alston and Askrigg Blocks clearly have different magnetic properties. The Weardale granite has no associated magnetic anomaly, whereas the Wensleydale granite and its westward projection beneath the Lake District show as a clear positive anomaly that links to a series of magnetic highs in the SE of the area of Figure 2.2. This regional system of positive anomalies must represent magnetic material either intruding deeper weakly magnetic sediments, or the sedimentary cover over crystalline basement in this area must be thinner than farther north.

Question 2.4 Substituting in Equation 2.2:

$$d = \frac{x_d}{2}\sqrt{\frac{S_2 - S_1}{S_2 + S_1}} \text{ gives}$$

$$35 = \frac{x_d}{2}\sqrt{\frac{1.5}{14.5}}$$

Rearranging:

$$x_d = \frac{35 \times 2}{\sqrt{\dfrac{1.5}{14.5}}} = \frac{70}{0.322} = 217 \text{ km}$$

So, a seismic refraction study of the entire continental crust needs survey lines at least 217 km long for each source of seismic energy.

Question 2.5 (a) The mantle maintains a uniform seismic-wave speed of 8 km s^{-1} everywhere beneath the Moho, but the lower crust (7 km s^{-1}) breaks down as a coherent layer south of the Southern Uplands Fault. (b) This boundary in the upper crust marks a displacement of the a_0/a_1 layer boundary or an abrupt thinning of a_1 to the south. The mid-crustal a_1 layer shows a reduced seismic-wave speed to the south of the boundary, as does the upper a_0 layer. (c) A change in speed of the a_0 layer takes place just to the south of the Highland Boundary Fault.

Question 2.6 (a) Both show marked horizontal changes in the number of reflectors in the crust between about 5 to 10 seconds two-way time. Common to both is a boundary between abundant reflectors from 5 to 10 seconds two-way time in the south, and fewer reflectors to the north. That boundary dips northwards in both profiles. (b) The NEC profile shows a similar, almost parallel boundary, where reflector density falls sharply to the south. The two boundaries define a zone of intensely reflecting crust that covers a horizontal distance of about 30 km, and which dips northwards as a distinct unit on the seismic profile. Both to the north and the south of this zone, the lower crust shows abundant reflectors in the lowermost part of the crust.

Question 2.7 Both profiles (a) and (b) show a prominent, though narrow, zone of reflectors that dips southwards from close to the inferred surface outcrop of the Variscan Front. There can be little doubt about a direct connection. The zone on (a) dips at a constant angle (note: this is not the true angle of its dip, because depth is shown as two-way time) to join a deep-crustal zone of densely packed, horizontal reflectors. On profile (b), the dip changes from relatively steep to relatively gentle at about 45 km from the north end of the profile. From there it dips gently southwards to merge with the deep-crustal reflectors. Although there are a few reflectors in the mantle beneath the Moho in the southern 100 km of profile (a), they show no organization that might suggest a continuation into the mantle of the structure related to the Variscan Front.

Question 2.8 (a) This is an area with strongly positive Bouguer gravity and magnetic anomalies, which suggests it is underlain by high-density rocks that are highly magnetic. It occupies the western part of North Wales. Close to this point, MAG shows a small elliptical feature. On the Tectonic Map, the region with high potential field anomalies roughly coincides with the darker blue EP_{1-2} unit in the Legend, which signifies Cambrian to Ordovician ages for the exposed rocks. There are many symbols indicating arc volcanic complexes of this age, plus abundant patches of the purple tone that signifies 'diorite, basic and ultrabasic intrusions'. The magnetic high is explained by this abundance of crystalline igneous rocks. The elliptical feature on MAG coincides with a similar shaped fault on the Tectonic Map, the outcrop of which suggests that it is folded. Because EP_{1-2} represents the Early Paleozoic sedimentary and volcanic rocks, which the Caledonian orogeny deformed, it is probably a thin veneer relative to the total thickness of the crust. The broad gravity high cannot be explained by the outcrops, and represents abnormally dense crust beneath the area. (b) On both GRAV and MAG, the point is within a roughly NE–SW-trending elliptical zone where both potential fields are abnormally low. On the Tectonic Map, this feature roughly coincides with the Cheshire Basin, with stratigraphic units LP_3–EM_1 and a small patch of EM_2 (Permian and Triassic to Jurassic) at the surface. The best explanation is that the potential-field anomalies result from a deep basin of Younger Cover. (c) The major feature between these points is a broad NE–SW zone with magnetically variable structure. It would be possible to sketch a curved line along the eastern boundary of this feature that might mark a major fault. By itself, GRAV does not show much except a change from positive anomalies to the NW that gradually change to negative towards the SE. However, there is a subtle feature, shadowed by the simulated illumination from the NW, that closely follows the eastern boundary of the magnetic feature. On the Tectonic Map, both features are close to the Church Stretton Fault and the Pontesford Lineament. They are drawn in pale blue, signifying 'Acadian Phase' structures (Lower to Middle Devonian). The magnetic feature and, to a lesser extent, its gravitational equivalent, suggest that these faults divide different kinds of hidden basement.

Question 2.9 Neither gravity nor magnetic data give clues to the location of the Iapetus Suture, and the only geological evidence for its rough position is the difference in Cambrian to Ordovician fossils between rocks of Northern England and those of the Southern Uplands. Seismic refraction data suggest that the rough line of the Southern Uplands Fault marks a change in the seismic wave speed of different crustal layers. Seismic reflection data, backed up by electrical properties of the crust, show prominent features in the upper to lower crust that define

a zone which dips northwards from the line joining the Solway and north Northumberland. In the case of the Variscan, a deep, negative magnetic anomaly fringes the southern coast of England, intersecting it at Start Point and the Lizard, where the Tectonic Map indicates highly metamorphosed rocks and an ophiolite respectively. A regional positive anomaly in the gravitational field roughly follows the magnetic trend. Over Cornwall, there is a linear system of negative gravity anomalies, which relate in part to the granites of Cornwall. Seismic reflection profiles across the gravity and magnetic anomalies show a steep northwards thrust near the Lizard. The thrust appears to affect the Moho.

Question 3.1 The trends for the four sets of orogenic belts in the > 2.5 to 1.0 Ga range are truncated at high angles by the western limit. At several points along the western limit there are occurrences of Precambrian sedimentary rocks spanning the period from 800 to 1400 Ma (at R in Alaska, in Montana, M and Death Valley, DV).

Question 3.2 In the same manner as Avalonia, Armorica rifted from northern Gondwana, but later during the Ordovician. It moved in the same general direction as Avalonia, and so sea-floor spreading must have been situated between it and Gondwana (by a shift in the eastern spreading axis of the Rheic Ocean on Figure 3.7c). For Armorica to move towards Laurentia implies that subduction at the Laurentian side of the Rheic Ocean must have occurred again and again.

Question 3.3 A sliver containing part of NE North America and what became the bulk of England and Wales moved with sinistral strike–slip relative to Laurentia in the period between 440 and 425 Ma, more or less to complete the framework of modern British geology, by sliding Scotland into its present position. Baltica had also moved with a similar sense to lie directly adjacent to the British Isles.

Question 3.4 On Figure 3.4, northern Britain lay at the equator at 750 Ma. By 580 Ma (Figure 3.6), it had moved to south polar latitudes, then steadily moved northwards towards the tropics during the Cambrian and Ordovician (Figure 3.7a to c), to remain fixed until the start of the Devonian (Figures 3.7d and 3.9). At the start of Rodinia's break-up, what was to become southern Britain lay in the northern tropics (Figure 3.4). By 580 Ma, the Cadomian arc was forming in middle southern latitudes. It had moved to southern polar regions in the Cambrian and Early Ordovician (Figure 3.7), before its separation from Gondwana as Avalonia. Spreading of the Rheic Ocean then drove it northwards to the southern tropics at the time of its collision and unification with Laurentia (Figures 3.7 and 3.9). Clearly, both major parts of the

British Isles must have undergone large climatic changes as well as those related to tectonics over the 350 Ma of their evolution.

Question 4.1 (a) Compared with the Andean sample, that from the Lewisian has higher LREE and lower HREE, so that it has a higher ratio of LREE to HREE. (b) The only residual mineral in which HREE are compatible elements while LREE are incompatible is garnet (Block 3 and Figure 4.17).

Question 4.2 (a) In the video, you saw that the dykes that cut sharply across the Badcallian foliation of the Central Region are deformed at their margins; in fact, each dyke margin is a small shear zone that also deforms the adjoining gneisses. In places, wider zones of Badcallian gneisses became involved in steep ductile shear zones, such as the Canisp Shear Zone (Figure 4.2). Shear strain in them rotated the dykes into parallelism with compositional banding, and they are complexly folded together with the gneisses. Moreover, the anhydrous gneisses were converted into low-grade, hydrous mylonites. (b) Hydration of the gneisses along dyke margins and in the shear zones indicates the movement of hydrous fluids, probably derived from the underthrust Laxfordian block. As well as changing the minerals in the Badcallian gneisses, such fluid flow would also have transported heat, changing the gneisses' rheology in the shear zones from brittle to ductile.

Question 4.3 (a) Today, ^{40}K is by far the largest contributor (and always has been), with ^{238}U and ^{232}Th roughly equal, and ^{235}U almost insignificant. Since the first billion years of Earth's evolution the rapid decay of ^{235}U has seen it drop from second to last place in its contribution. The slow decay of ^{238}U and ^{232}Th has changed their heat production relatively little during Earth history. (b) At the time of accretion, 2000 Ma and 4000 Ma thereafter, total heat production was the sum of heat produced by each isotope ($^{40}K + {}^{238}U + {}^{232}Th + {}^{235}U$). At the time of accretion, 4550 Ma ago, this was $3.5 \times 10^{-5} + 2 \times 10^{-6} + 1.3 \times 10^{-6} + 3.4 \times 10^{-6} = \mathbf{4.17 \times 10^{-5}\,\mu W\,kg^{-1}}$; at 2550 Ma $1.4 \times 10^{-5} + 1.7 \times 10^{-6} + 1.2 \times 10^{-6} + 4 \times 10^{-7} = \mathbf{1.73 \times 10^{-5}\,\mu W\,kg^{-1}}$; at 550 Ma $3.7 \times 10^{-6} + 1 \times 10^{-6} + 1 \times 10^{-6} + 5 \times 10^{-8} = \mathbf{5.7 \times 10^{-6}\,\mu W\,kg^{-1}}$. Those values are joined by the straight line shown on Figure A4.1. (c) The plot of total heat production shows very little difference from that for ^{40}K, which has contributed more than 80% of radiogenic heat since the Earth formed. So uncertainty in the Earth's potassium content is the most critical, and permits speculation that some proportion of heat flow at the present is heat remaining from that released gravitationally by Earth's accretion and by core formation.

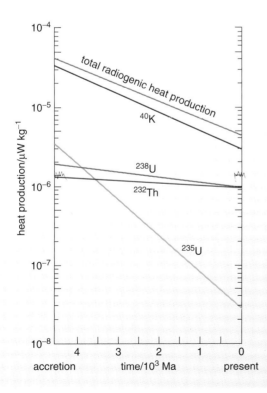

Figure A4.1 Plot of total radiogenic heat production through time.

Question 4.4 Estimated heat production today from Figure A4.1 is $4.2 \times 10^{-6}\ \mu\text{W kg}^{-1}$. At the time when the oldest rocks formed, it was $4.2 \times 10^{-5}\ \mu\text{W kg}^{-1}$, or 10 times greater. At the end of the Archean, the value of 1.8^{-5} $\mu\text{W kg}^{-1}$ is about 4 times greater. By the beginning of Phanerozoic times, heat production of $5.7 \times 10^{-6}\ \mu\text{W kg}^{-1}$ was 1.4 times greater than at present.

Question 4.5 Figure A4.2 shows a slab-temperature plot (green) associated with higher heat flow, which reaches higher temperatures at shallower depths. The critical point on the diagram is where the 'wet' basalt solidus and the amphibole-out lines cross. If the slab-temperature plot is at higher temperature and lower pressure than this, partial melting of the slab occurs before the onset of dehydration. The greater the increase in temperature with depth, the wider the gap between the 'wet' basalt solidus and the conditions for dehydration of amphibole. This implies that at some time in the past, when mean global heat flow was higher than now, the probability of slab melting was higher than it is today. The higher the heat flow, the longer the path of the 'wet' slab through conditions that can induce it to partially melt.

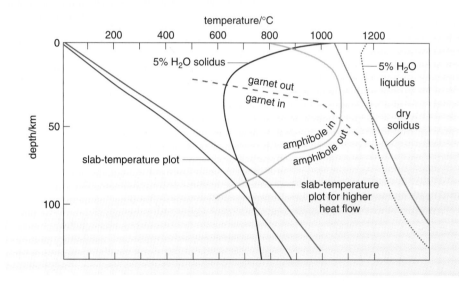

Figure A4.2 Figure 4.12 showing a slab-temperature plot for higher heat flow at a subduction zone (shown in green).

Question 4.6 (a) With the given assumptions, heat flow would need to be twice that for 80-Ma-old modern oceanic lithosphere, or about $100\ \text{mW m}^{-2}$ to prevent eclogite formation. That is equivalent to an age of roughly 20 Ma from Figure 4.14. (b) For 20-Ma-old lithosphere to reach subduction zones on average, heat production would need to be about 4 times the present value. From Figure 4.11a, that would have occurred before about 4000 Ma ago.

Question 4.7 You could have considered these main possibilities: 1. If oceanic lithosphere was generally warmer than now, it would have been less dense, so that the sea-floor was topographically higher. That would reduce the volume of the ocean basins, resulting in seawater flooding the continents. 2. A thinner continental crust would rise to lower elevations than today, so increasing the likelihood of widespread flooding. 3. Mafic to ultramafic lavas would form a layer of higher density than the underlying crust, causing the crust to subside. 4. Extension of the continental crust would form subsiding basins.

Question 4.8 The topographic elevation of the continental surface creates gravitational forces away from the highest areas. Those forces result in extensional stress. Increases in elevation can result either from mountain building or doming because of the thermal effect of plumes rising to the base of the lithosphere. The first occurs in the Tibetan Plateau and elsewhere in the Alpine–Himalayan orogen (Block 4, Section 7.4). A classic case of the second is the formation of the East African Rift and the Red Sea (Block 2, Section 3.7).

Question 4.9 (a) Archean felsic rocks show strong depletion in heavy rare-earth elements. The only common mineral that shows K_d values greater than 1.0 for heavy rare-earth elements is garnet. (b) Archean felsic igneous rocks do not show negative Eu anomalies, and neither do Archean shales that formed by erosion of the upper continental crust. Because Eu is strongly partitioned from melts into feldspars, Archean evidence rules out feldspar fractionation. (c) Greenstone belts contain mafic and ultramafic lavas that have unusually high magnesium contents. Increasing magnesium content signifies higher degrees of partial melting, higher potential temperatures and melting at shallower levels. (d) Feldspar, along with ferromagnesian silicates, imparts strength to the lithosphere, whereas rocks containing large amounts of quartz reduce lithospheric strength. The lack of evidence for feldspar fractionation in Archean felsic rocks implies the absence of any feldspar-rich layer in the deep crust. Rather than being highly evolved, Archean crust formed by a single stage of slab melting. Likely to be quartz-rich throughout, the Archean crust would have weakened the continental lithosphere.

Question 4.10 (a) The three regions of the Lewisian differ in age by 200 Ma, and could not have formed during the same event. Large shear zones that separate the three regions can therefore be explained at sutures. (b) The Gairloch Shear Zone, separating the Central and Southern Regions, is related to a series of 1900-Ma-old metasedimentary and volcanic rocks, whose structural relationships and composition suggest that they formed in an accretionary prism associated with a destructive margin. The age (1750 Ma) of deformation in the Laxford and Gairloch Shear Zones suggests collision between the three components at the same time, when any intervening oceanic lithosphere had been totally subducted.

Question 5.1 Pink PP_3 occurs next to pink-grey NP_{2-3} (Neoproterozoic) in these small areas. That is the Dalradian Supergroup. The contacts are faults, i.e. tectonic boundaries.

Question 5.2 The total thickness of the Dalradian Supergroup given by Figure 5.5 is around 32 km. Taken at face value, such a thickness implies that during the later evolution of the Dalradian basin the lowermost Grampian Group would have been at a depth close to that of the Moho beneath normal continental crust. At such depths, the Grampian Group would inevitably have suffered high-grade metamorphism, perhaps beginning to melt.

Question 5.3 In the oldest conglomerates, the dominant lithologies are mafic to ultramafic in composition, presumably derived from uplifted ophiolite. Higher in the sequence, clasts of granitic to dioritic composition increase in abundance, particularly among the larger boulders. Small pebbles of fine-grained felsic igneous rocks appear and become more abundant upwards.

Question 5.4 (a) Deposition of monotonous mudstones in deep water went on during the Early Ordovician, followed by a break in sedimentation. Renewed deposition began in shallow-water conditions, soon to be followed by submarine volcanic activity. (b) South-west Wales reverted to nearshore sedimentation after early volcanism, then deposition beneath deepening water interrupted by submarine volcanism during the Middle Ordovician, followed by continuous deposition of

turbidites, presumably from an unstable submarine slope. North Wales follows much the same pattern of fining and deepening-upwards marine sedimentation, but volcanism only occurred during the Late Ordovician. The last involved emergence and subaerial volcanic activity that produced the lavas and ashes of the Snowdon area. (c) For much of the Ordovician, Shropshire was an area of non-deposition, being on the margin of the Midland Platform. Late Ordovician sedimentation was nearshore, above storm wave base. (d) Deep-water mudstones dominate the early part of the Ordovician of the Lake District, but these conditions were interrupted from the Middle Ordovician onwards by periods of volcanic activity, culminating in subaerial volcanic activity to form the Borrowdale Volcanic Group in the Late Ordovician.

Question 5.5 There is no sign of any Acadian deformation, weak or intense, in rocks younger than about 380 Ma (Late Devonian). Intense deformation varies in timing a great deal. There is no evidence shown for it in the Highlands (but see later) and only weak folding seems to have affected Northern Ireland and the Midland Valley. It ended first in the Longford-Down (Ireland) and Southern Uplands before the start of the Devonian (about 430 Ma), and last in Wales in the Early Devonian (about 405 Ma). Weak deformation ended last in the Lake District, about 382 Ma ago.

Question 5.6 From the presence of muscovite (and cordierite) in the mode, and of corundum in the norm, the granites are peraluminous. They are likely to be related to continental collision (Blocks 3 and 4).

Question 5.7 The granites' initial $^{87}Sr/^{86}Sr$ ratios are all higher than that of the contemporary mantle, so a crustal component is implied. The metasediments have generally higher values that are too high to be the sole source of the granite. There are two possibilities: (i) the melts result from a mixture between mantle and crustal melts; (ii) the granites are pure crustal melts but from a deeper lithology within the crust which had lower $^{87}Sr/^{86}Sr$ ratios.

Question 5.8 The K-rich basaltic dykes and lavas in South-West England resemble the Neogene volcanics from northern Tibet (Block 4, Section 7.4.4). Those resulted from convective thinning of the lithosphere following collision and tectonic thickening. It is possible that, after the Variscan Orogeny, convective thinning of the lithosphere led to uplift and then collapse of the thickened crust during its extension. Convective thinning would also have induced heating and melting of the sub-lithospheric mantle to generate basaltic magmas. The granites could have resulted from melting of the lower crust because of greatly increased heat flow from the rising basaltic magma.

Question 5.9 The basement to the Northern Highland Terrane is Archean, whereas that underlying the Grampian terrane is Proterozoic in age. There are no occurrences of the Dalradian Supergroup north of the Great Glen Fault. The two terranes only show similar geological histories at the time of the Grampian Orogeny (although the Central Highland Migmatites of the Grampian Terrane formed at the same time as the peak of Moine metamorphism).

Question 5.10 Its complete stratigraphic sequence approaches the thickness of normal continental crust, so that by the time the youngest parts were being deposited, the oldest part of a complete sequence would have been at temperatures and pressures that would encourage partial melting. Also, there are no known sedimentary sequences that span 300 Ma without any tectonic breaks.

Question 5.11 The Southern Uplands terrane comprises several blocks, divided by southward-directed thrusts. The latest age of fine-grained, deep-water sediments decreases towards the south. Both features are compatible with the terrane's having formed as an accretionary prism above a zone of northward subduction.

Question 5.12 The Devonian magmatism has arc-like affinities but post-dates the Caledonian Orogeny, when subduction along the Iapetus Suture had ceased. A possible explanation is that partial melting in the mantle wedge was triggered by delamination of mantle lithosphere beneath the British Isles.

Question 5.13 The Highland Border Complex contains ophiolites, suggesting that oceanic lithosphere was obducted onto the Grampian Terrane during the Grampian Orogeny. Sediments within the Complex show no signs of debris derived from the evolving Grampian Terrane, nor deformation and metamorphism that the now close-by Dalradian Supergroup underwent in the Early Ordovician. In fact, marine sediments continued to accumulate in the Complex until well after the climax of the Grampian orogeny. The Highland Border Complex must have been emplaced by strike–slip movements.

Question 5.14 Each separated from Gondwana at different times between the Neoproterozoic and Silurian, as marginal slivers split off by extensional tectonics and then sea-floor spreading close to the margin of Gondwana. The closest modern analogue is the formation of the East African Rift and the Red Sea (Block 2).

Question 5.15 Lower Paleozoic rocks involved in the Caledonian orogeny are intruded by calc-alkaline granites dated between 430–400 Ma. Devonian and Carboniferous rocks of Variscan SW England were intruded by peralkaline granites of the Cornubian

Batholith between 300 and 270 Ma. The two suites have different Sr isotope compositions. The post-Caledonian granites have generally low initial $^{87}Sr/^{86}Sr$ ratios, clearly indicating their formation from a source in the mantle, with variable and minor crustal contamination. Granites of the Cornubian Batholith have much higher values of the ratio, which suggest that a large proportion of the magma formed by crustal melting.

Question 6.1 It suggests that active subsidence was taking place (to permit such large thicknesses of sediments to accumulate), and it also suggests that sediment and magma supplies were simultaneously available.

Question 6.2 Virtually all of the compositions on Figure 6.10 lie above the alkaline-subalkaline dividing line, and are alkaline. A few lie within the transitional field. The bulk of the rocks are basalts (SiO_2 45–52%), but there are some more evolved (felsic) compositions and also some rocks with lower SiO_2 content than basalt (i.e. <45% SiO_2). The fractionation trend towards hawaiite, mugearite, and eventually trachyte, phonolite, and rhyolite, is also consistent with the alkalic nature of the parental basalts (cf. Block 2, Figure 2.2).

Question 6.3 The xenoliths would probably have been resorbed or assimilated into the basalt magma. The crystal fragments would have re-equilibrated — for example, above 70 km the aluminium in the mantle garnets would have contributed to spinel formation at the expense of garnet, and then to plagioclase formation at near-surface pressures (see Block 2, Figure 2.10).

Question 6.4 (a) The MPG lavas have the widest range of MgO contents, from 21% down to less than 1%, compared with 7.5–12.5% for the CG and 3.5–8% for the CMT. There are broad similarities between the CaO contents of the MPG and CG but the CG lavas tend to have higher CaO contents for a given MgO and the CMT lavas have distinctly higher CaO contents for a given MgO. In terms of the Na_2O contents, all three groups illustrate a negative trend between Na_2O and MgO, but both the CG and CMT have lower Na_2O contents for a given MgO content. (b) The Mg# is the ratio of molar Mg to molar Mg and Fe^{2+} (Block 2, Section 2.5.1). Lavas with Mg# greater than 65 are in equilibrium with olivine with a forsterite content greater than Fo_{88} (i.e. mantle olivine). The plot of Mg# versus MgO (Figure 6.17c) shows that none of the CMT basalts could have been in equilibrium with the mantle. The most magnesian of the CG basalts and all of the MPG basalts above 13% MgO might just have been in equilibrium with the mantle. Therefore, those basalts are both primitive and primary in nature, being the most MgO-rich lavas in the sequence (primitive) and may not have suffered any fractional crystallization (primary).

Question 6.5 Figure 2.17 in Block 2 shows how the pressure and temperature of partial melting of a typical mantle peridotite can be estimated from SiO_2 and MgO. Using a SiO_2 content of 46% and a MgO content of 15% gives a pressure of 3 GPa and a temperature of ~1400 °C for the melting of the primary Mull basalts.

Question 6.6 The lavas with the highest MgO content also have the highest, most radiogenic $^{87}Sr/^{86}Sr$ ratios. This implies that the hottest, most primitive lavas have suffered more crustal contamination than the more evolved lavas. AFC processes result in the most evolved magmas assimilating more crustal material. The ATA process is therefore the most likely means for crustal contamination in this case.

Question 6.7 The SMV formed in a passive margin setting as a result of lithospheric extension, whereas the BTIP represents active margin processes that involved the influence of a long-lived mantle plume.

Question 6.8 Pyroxenite and garnet fragments remain in the lavas. This signifies that magma ascent was rapid, otherwise these mantle materials would have been absorbed by the magma. Rapid ascent also makes it less easy for magmas to pick up and assimilate crustal materials before they erupt. In fact, the SMV lavas do contain barely altered xenoliths from the full range of crustal levels.

Acknowledgements

Every effort has been made to trace all copyright owners, but if any has been inadvertently overlooked, we will be pleased to make the necessary arrangements at the earliest opportunity. Grateful acknowledgement is made to the following sources for permission to reproduce material within this Block:

Figure 2.1 S. A. Drury, Open University; *Figure 2.5* F. W. Dunning *et al.* (1978) 'Britain before man', HMSO for the Institute of Geological Sciences, Crown copyright reproduced under Licence CO1W0000065 with permission of the Controller of HMSO and the Queen's Printer for Scotland; *Figure 2.6* P. Kearey and M. Brooks (1984) 'An introduction to geophysical exploration', *Geophysical Texts*, Vol. 4, Blackwell; *Figures 2.8–2.10* D. Bamford *et al.* (1978) 'LISPB-IV Crustal structure of Northern Britain', *Geophysical Journal of The Royal Astronomical Society*, **54**, Blackwell; *Figure 2.12* NERC (1988) British Institutions Reflection Profiling Syndicate Prospectus as at October 1988 from UK and Overseas Experiments during 1989–1993; *Figure 2.13a* J. A. Brewer *et al.* (1983) 'BIRPS deep seismic reflection studies...', *Nature*, **305**; *Figure 2.13b,c* B. Freeman, S. L. Klemperer and R. W. Hobbs (1988) 'The deep structure of northern England...', *Journal of the Geological Society, London*, **145**; *Figure 2.13d* S. L. Klemperer and D. H. Matthews (1987) 'Iapetus Suture located beneath the North Sea by BIRPS', in *Geology*, **15**, The Geological Society of America; *Figure 2.14* BIRPS and ECORS (1986) 'Deep seismic reflection profiling...', *Journal of the Geological Society London*, **143**; *Figures 3.2, 3.3* E. M. Moores (1991) 'Southwest U.S. – East Antarctica (SWEAT) connection...', *Geology*, **19**, The Geological Society of America; *Figures 3.4, 3.6* Dalziel (1992) and Torsvik *et al.* (1996); *Figure 3.5a* R. J. Stern (1994) 'Arc assembly and continental collision...', *Annual Review of Earth and Planetary Sciences*, **22**, © Annual Reviews Inc.; *Figures 3.7, 3.9* Ronald Blakey, Northern Arizona University; *Figure 3.8* L. R. M. Cocks *et al.* (1997) 'The margins of Avalonia', *Geological Magazine*, **134** © Cambridge University Press; *Figure 4.2* M. P. Coward *et al.* (1987) 'The evolution of the Lewisian...', *Geological Society Special Publication*, **27**, The Geological Society; *Figure 4.3* B. L. Weaver and J. Tarney (1980) 'Rare earth geochemistry...', *Earth and Planetary Science Letters*, **51**, Elsevier; *Figure 4.4* J. G. Arth and G. N. Hanson (1972) 'Quartz diorites derived by partial melting', *Contributions to Mineralogy and Petrology*, **7**, Springer-Verlag; *Figures 4.5, 4.12, 4.13* H. Martin (1986) 'Effect of steeper Archaean...', *Geology*, **14**, The Geological Society of America; *Figure 4.7* S. R. Taylor and S. M. McLennan (1985) *The Continental Crust: Its Composition and Evolution*, Blackwell; *Figure 4.8* from an article by M. P. Coward and R. G. Park in R. G. Park and J. Tarney (eds) (1987) *The Evolution of the Lewisian and Comparable Precambrian High Grade Terraces*, Special Publication, Vol. 27, The Geological Society, London; *Figure 4.9* C. A. Stein (1995) 'Heat flow of the Earth', *AGU reference shelf series*, **1**, American Geophysical Union; *Figure 4.14* M. J. Bickle (1978) 'Heat loss from the Earth', *Earth and Planetary Science Letters*, **40**, Elsevier; *Figures 4.15–4.19* T. Komiya *et al.* (1999) 'Plate tectonics at 3.8–3.7 Ga...', *Journal of Geology*, **17**, University of Chicago Press; *Figure 4.21* D. Chardon *et al.* (1988) 'Sinking of the Dharwar Basin...', *Precambrian Research*, **91**, Elsevier; *Figure 5.1* R. G. Park (1991) 'The Lewisian Complex' in G. Y. Craig (ed.) *Geology of Scotland*, The Geological Society, London; *Figure 5.2* redrawn after P. G. Nicholson (1993) 'A basin reappraisal of the Proterozoic Torridon Group...' in L. E. Frostick and R. J. Steel (eds) *Tectonic controls and signatures in sedimentary successions*, Blackwell, *Figures 5.3, 5.7–5.9, 5.11–5.16* R. A. Woodcock and R. A. Strachan (eds) (2000) *Geological History of Britain and Ireland*, Blackwell; *Figure 5.4* N.J. Soper *et al.* (1998) 'Tectonostratigraphy of the Moine Supergroup...', *Journal of the Geological Society London*, **155**; *Figure 5.5* R. Anderton (1985) 'Sedimentation and tectonics...', *Scottish Journal of Geology*, **21**; *Figure 5.10* D. B. Snyder and A. J. Barber (1997) 'Australasian Banda Arc collision...', *Journal of the Geological Society London*, **154**; *Figure 5.18* A. L. Harris (1985) 'The nature and timing of orogenic activity...', *Memoirs of the Geological Society, London*, **9**; *Figure 5.19* S. P. Todd *et al.* (1991) 'On the trace of the Iapetus Suture...', *Journal of the Geological Society London*, **148**; *Figure 5.21* Dee Edwards, Open University; *Figure 5.22b* J. Willis-Richards and N. J. Jackson (1989) 'Evolution of the Cornubian ore field...', © *Economic Geology*, **84**, Economic Geologists Publishing Co., *Figure 6.1* E. H. Francis (1978) 'The Midland Valley as a rift...', in I. B. Ramberg and E. R. Neuman (eds), *Tectonics and Geophysics of Continental Rifts*, Kluwer; *Figure 6.2* F. W. Anderton (1951) 'The Geological Survey bore at Rashiehill, Stirlingshire' *Bull. Geol. Surv. G.B.*, **20**, pp.43–106; *Figure 6.3* W. Mykura (1967) 'The Upper Carboniferous rocks of SW Ayrshire', *Bull. Geol. Surv. G.B.*, **26**, pp.23–98; *Figure 6.4* by permission of the Royal Geological Society of Edinburgh and G. J. Upton, P. Aspen and R. H. Hunter, 'Xenoliths and their implications...', *Transactions*, **75**; *Figure 6.5* E. H. Francis (1983) 'Carboniferous–Permian igneous rocks', in G. Y. Craig (ed.), *Geology of Scotland*, Scottish Academic Press; *Figure 6.6 a, b* Dave McGarvie, Open University; *Figures 6.6c, 6.8* I. B. Cameron and D. Stephenson (1985) *British Regional Geology Series: The Midland Valley of Scotland*, H.M.S.O. for the British Geological Survey/NERC; *Figure 6.7* E. H. Francis (1983) in G. Y. Craig (ed.) *Geology of Scotland*, Scottish Academic Press, from H. A. F. de Souza (1979) 'The geochronology of Scottish Carboniferous volcanism', unpub. Ph.D. thesis, University of Edinburgh; *Figure 6.9* E. H. Francis (1983) in G. Y. Craig (ed) *Geology of Scotland*, Scottish Academic Press, originally from I. B. Ramberg and R. R. Neumann (eds) (1978) *Tectonics and Geophysics of Continental Rifts*, 133–147, Reidel, Holland; *Figure 6.10* R. MacDonald (1975) 'Petrochemistry of the Early Carboniferous...', *Scottish Journal of Geology*, XI, Pt 4, Scottish Academic Press; *Figure 6.13* R. W. Kent and J. G. Fitton (2000) 'Mantle sources and melting dynamics in the British Palaeogene Igneous Province', *Journal of Petrology*, **41**(7), Oxford University Press; *Figure 6.14* J. E. Richey *et al.* (1930) 'The geology of Ardnamurchan' in *Memoir of the Geological Survey*, by permission of the Director, Institute of Geological Sciences; *Figures 6.15, 6.17–6.21* Andy Kerr, Cardiff University; *Figure 6.16* M. A. Hamilton *et al.* (1998) 'Rapid eruption of Skye lavas...', *Nature*, **394**.

Index